MEASURING CLINICAL CARE

A Guide for Physician Executives

Edited by Stephen C. Schoenbaum, MD, MPH

American College of Physician Executives
Suite 200
4890 West Kennedy Boulevard
Tampa, Florida 33609
(813) 287-2000

ISBN: 0-924674-36-9

Library of Congress Card Number: 95-77379

Printed in the United States of America by Hillsboro Printing Company, Tampa, Florida.

About the Authors

Donald M. Berwick, MD, MPP, is President and CEO of the Institute for Healthcare Improvement, Boston, Mass., a not-for-profit organization dedicated to helping accelerate the pace of improvement in the U.S. and Canadian health care systems. He is a practicing physician at the Harvard Community Health Plan; an Associate in Pediatrics at Children's Hospital, Boston; and a Consultant in Pediatrics at Massachusetts General Hospital. He is Associate Professor of Pediatrics at Harvard Medical School and Adjunct Associate Professor of Health Policy and Management at Harvard School of Public Health. Dr. Berwick served as the principal investigator for the National Demonstration Project on Quality Improvement, a pioneering effort to introduce the methods and tools of quality improvement to the health care industry. He holds a bachelor's degree from Harvard College, a master's degree in public policy from the John F. Kennedy School of Government, and a medical degree from Harvard Medical School.

David Blumenthal, MD, MPP, is Chief, Health Policy Research and Development Unit, and Associate Physician, Massachusetts General Hospital, Boston, Mass. He is also Associate Professor of Medicine and Associate Professor of Health Care Policy at Harvard Medical School. He previously was Senior Vice President, Brigham and Women's Hospital, Boston. He served as chief health advisor to the Dukakis presidential campaign and was Executive Director of the Center for Health Policy and Management and Lecturer on Public Policy at the John F. Kennedy School of Government at Harvard. Dr. Blumenthal's research interests include health care quality management, determinants of physician behavior, access to health services, and the extent and consequences of academic-industrial relationships in the health sciences.

Bruce E. Bradley, MBA, is Corporate Manager-Managed Care for GTE Corporation, where he is responsible for executing the company's health care cost containment strategies, including development and management of managed care plans and strategies and implementation of an integrated health care information system. Prior to his present position, Mr. Bradley was President and CEO of Rhode Island Group Health Association and Executive Director of Matthew Thornton Health Plan. He received his bachelor's degree from Yale University and his MBA from the Wharton School of the University of Pennsylvania.

Roberta N. Clarke, PhD, MBA, is Associate Professor and former Chairman of the Department of Marketing at Boston University's School of Management. Professor Clarke teaches health care marketing courses in Boston University's Health Care Management Program and in its School of Medicine. She is coauthor of *Marketing for Health Care Organizations*, a leading text in the field of health care marketing. Professor Clarke received her master's degree in business administration and her doctorate from the Harvard Graduate School of Business Administration.

i

Janet M. Corrigan, PhD, MBA, is a Principal Researcher with the Center for Studying Health System Change in Washington, D.C., an applied research organization whose primary purpose is to gather and analyze information on the impact of health system changes on the populations of selected communities. Dr. Corrigan's research has been concentrated in the area of managed care, with particular emphasis on quality of care, health status, and consumer satisfaction issues. Prior to joining the Center, Dr. Corrigan was Vice President for Planning and Development for the National Committee for Quality Assurance, a quality oversight organization for the managed care industry. Dr. Corrigan received a PhD degree in health services organization and policy and a master's degree in industrial engineering from the University of Michigan. She also has a master's in business administration and a master's in community health from the University of Rochester.

Charles M. Cutler, MD, MS, is Vice President of Medical Services, Prudential Insurance Company of America, Roseland, N.J. He previously was Deputy Medical Director and Vice President for Medical Programs at Harvard Community Health Plan of New England, Providence, RI, and Chief of the Department of Internal Medicine and Medical Director of the Rhode Island Group Health Association, which became the Harvard Community Health Plan of New England. He is an instructor in medicine and community health at Brown University. He is a reviewer for the National Committee on Quality Assurance and a member of the Committee on Quality Health Care of the Group Health Association of America. Dr. Cutler received his bachelor's degree from the University of Chicago and his medical degree from New York University.

Helen Darling is Manager, Healthcare Strategy and Programs, Xerox Corporation, with responsibility for the broad strategic directions of health programs, for implementing the Xerox health care strategy, and for managing its fee-for-service plan. She previously was Principal in the health care practice of William M. Mercer in its Stamford, Conn., office. She served as senior health policy and health benefits advisor to U.S. Senator David Durenberger and as Vice President of Government Research Corporation, a public policy consulting firm. Ms. Darling has a master's degree in demography/sociology from Memphis State University.

Joseph M. Healy Jr., PhD, is Director of Quality and Outcomes Measurement, Corporate Medical Director's Office, Harvard Community Health Plan, Boston, Mass. He completed his doctoral training in psychological research at Boston University and a postdoctoral fellowship in human motivation at Harvard University. He was involved in the design of some of the first patient satisfaction tools used at Harvard Community Health Plan and spent several years teaching and conducting research on stress, coping, and adaptation to traumatic life events. His responsibilities at Harvard Community Health Plan have included patient-based quality measurement, guideline development, and quality consulting. He is currently leading efforts to develop, evaluate, and implement a variety of patient-based measures of health care processes, outcomes, and satisfaction in support of efforts to monitor and improve the quality of care at Harvard Community Health Plan.

Frederic G. Jones, MD, FACPE, is Executive Vice President for Medical Affairs, Anderson Area Medical Center, Anderson, S.C. He is a Fellow of the American College of Physician Executives and a Diplomate of the American Board of Medical Management. His major interest has been education-based physician practice analysis and the use of statistical process control in clinical process improvement. Dr. Jones, a cardiologist, serves as Director of Medical Education and Professor of Family Medicine and Assistant Dean at the Medical University of South Carolina.

Lisa I. Iezzoni, MD, MSc, is an Associate Professor of Medicine at Harvard Medical School and Codirector of Research in the Division of General Medicine and Primary Care, Department of Medicine, Beth Israel Hospital, Boston, Mass. She has conducted numerous studies for the Health Care Financing Administration, the Agency for Health Care Policy and Research, and private foundations on a variety of topics, including the use of clinical data to predict hospitalization costs and patient outcomes, comparing severity of illness across teaching and nonteaching hospitals, evaluating the utility of severity information for quality assessment, and using information from hospital data systems to predict patient clinical and functional outcomes and satisfaction with care. She recently published *Risk Adjustment for Measuring Health Care Outcomes,* an introductory text on risk adjustment methodologies. Dr. Iezzoni received her degrees in medicine and health policy and management from Harvard University.

Dwight N. McNeill is Healthcare Information Manager, GTE Corporation, where he is responsible for the development and utilization of health care information systems that report on costs, quality, and outcomes in support of corporate health care strategy. Prior to joining GTE, he was a director at MEDSTAT Systems, a vice president of a chemical dependency treatment facility, and an evaluative researcher in the field of mental health. He was on the Steering Committee of the NCQA Report Card Project, is a member of the HEDIS 3.0 Committee, is a member of the Executive Committee of the MHCA Outcomes Management Systems Project, and is cochairman of the founding committee for the Foundation for Accountability.

William F. Minogue, MD, FACP, is Senior Vice President for Medical Affairs, Suburban Hospital, Bethesda, Md. Previously, he was Vice President for Clinical Affairs for the Bon Secours Health System, Marriotsville, Md., and Medical Director for George Washington University Hospital, Washington, D.C. Dr. Minogue was a member of the Task Force on Organization and Management Effectiveness of the Joint Commission on Accreditation of Healthcare Organizations and served as Chair of the Joint Commission's Task Force on Quality Improvement. The latter group developed a set of principles that were used to write the 1992-1995 performance improvement standards for all health care organizations surveyed by the Joint Commission.

Colletta H. (K.K.) Moore, MS, Consultant, QualPro, Knoxville, Tenn., has extensive experience in statistical methods, process improvement, and training and education in the health care industry. She has authored and coauthored manual texts for QualPro seminars, including *Basic Statistical Quality Improvement Techniques for the Health Care*

Industry and Experimental Design Techniques for Service Processes. She earned a B.S. degree in mathematics education and an M.S. degree in statistics from the University of Tennessee.

Gordon Mosser, MD, is a general internist and Executive Director, Institute for Clinical Systems Integration (ICSI), Minneapolis, Minn., a quality improvement organization that bridges Park Nicollet Medical Center, Group Health, Mayo Clinic, and 17 other medical groups in Minneapolis-St. Paul and nearby areas. ICSI has close ties to HealthPartners, an HMO, and to the Business Health Care Action Group, a consortium of 23 employers in Minnesota. ICSI's core activity is health care guideline development and implementation. Dr. Mosser graduated from Harvard College and Harvard Medical School.

Albert G. Mulley Jr., MD, MPP, is Associate Professor of Medicine and Associate Professor of Health Policy at Harvard Medical School and Chief of the General Internal Medicine Division and Director of the Medical Practices Evaluation Center at Massachusetts General Hospital, Boston. His recent research has focused on the uses of decision analysis, outcomes research, and preference assessment methods to distinguish between warrranted and unwarranted variations in clinical practice. Dr. Mulley's work has led to development of research instruments and approaches, including shared decision-making programs using interactive videodisk technology to inform patients about treatment options and to catalyze large-scale prospective clinical trials. He received his degrees in medicine and public policy from Harvard.

Stephen C. Schoenbaum, MD, MPH, is Medical Director, Harvard Community Health Plan of New England, Providence, R.I., where he is responsible for the medical program in a 90,000-member, staff and network model HMO. Previously, he served as Deputy Medical Director of Harvard Community Health Plan, the parent organization. In this position, he supervised departments for clinical quality management, clinical care measurement, health promotion and education, clinical publications, clinical risk management, and workers' health. Dr. Schoenbaum was a member of the committees that developed HEDIS 1.0 and 2.0. He is an Associate Professor of Medicine at the Harvard Medical School.

Paul M. Schyve, MD, is Senior Vice President of the Joint Commission on Accreditation of Healthcare Organizations, Oak Brook, Ill. He has also served as Vice President for Research and Standards and as Director of Standards for the Joint Commission. Prior to joining the Joint Commission, he was Clinical Director of the State of Illinois Department of Mental Health and Developmental Disabilities. Dr. Schyve received his undergraduate degree from the University of Rochester and his medical degree from the University of Rochester School of Medicine and Dentistry.

Cary Sennett, MD, PhD, is Vice President for Performance Measurement at the National Committee for Quality Assurance (NCQA), where he is responsible for overseeing NCQA's efforts to provide national leadership in initiatives to develop standards and tools to objectively assess the performance of managed care plans. He previously was a Medical Director at U.S. Healthcare and Vice President for Research and Development at U.S. Quality Algorithms, an information services subsidiary of U.S. Healthcare. He had responsibility for the development of sophisticated analytical methods to evaluate the quality of health care providers and was significantly involved in U.S. Healthcare's efforts to use these methods to support management efforts to improve the effectiveness and efficiency of its care. Dr. Sennett has also had quality leadership roles at Group Health Cooperative of Puget Sound and at Aetna Health Plans. A board-certified internist, he earned his medical degree from Yale University's School of Medicine and his PhD from Massachusetts Institute of Technology.

David N. Sundwall, MD, is President, American Clinical Laboratory Association, Washington, D.C., a national organization representing leading national, regional, and local independent clinical laboratories. Prior to this position, he was Vice President and Medical Director, American Healthcare Systems, a coalition of U.S. not-for-profit multihospital systems. He was formerly Administrator, Health Resources and Services Administration, Public Health Service, Department of Health and Human Services. He has academic appointments at the Uniformed Services University of the Health Sciences, Georgetown University College of Medicine, and University of Utah College of Medicine. Dr. Sundwall was cochair of the Work Group to Establish Medical Review Criteria, Performance Measures, and Quality Standards for Clinical Practice Guidelines for the Agency for Health Care Policy and Research.

Al Truscott, MD, is Medical Director, Group Health Cooperative of Puget Sound, where he leads the activities of more than 800 physicians and other medical staff members who provide services to 471,000 consumers. Prior to becoming medical director, Dr. Truscott served as Chief of Tacoma Specialty Center, Assistant Chief of Staff for Group Health's South Region, and South Region Chief of Staff. Board certified in obstetrics/gynecology, he received his undergraduate degree from Wesleyan University and his medical degree from the University of Southern California Medical School. He served his residency in obstetrics/gynecology at the Los Angeles County-University of Southern California Medical Center.

Steven Zatz, MD, is Medical Director of patient and disease management programs, U.S. Healthcare, Blue Bell, Pa. He previously directed U.S. Quality Algorithms, Inc., the quality management subsidiary of U.S. Healthcare. Prior to joining U.S. Healthcare, Dr. Zatz was a Director of Medical Services in the Group Department of Prudential Insurance Company of America. He was a member of the Agency for Health Care Policy and Research's Work Group to Develop Methods for Deriving Medical Review Criteria, Standards of Quality, and Performance Measures, and a member of the National Committee on Quality Assurance's Performance Assessment Committee. Dr. Zatz has an undergraduate degree in physics from Yale College and an MD degree from Cornell University Medical College.

ACKNOWLEDGMENTS

This book is dedicated to the memory of Alexander D. Langmuir, MD. Alex was the founding director of the epidemiology program at the Centers for Disease Control and Prevention (CDC) and the creator of the Epidemic Intelligence Service (EIS). He referred to himself simply as an epidemiologist, but, in fact, he was also a teacher and a talented physician executive who influenced and inspired hundreds of young physicians who had come to CDC to serve in the EIS. Alex was my mentor. He encouraged me as I moved from a career in traditional epidemiology to interests in medical management and the measurement and improvement of quality of care. The principles of surveillance and the techniques of "shoeleather epidemiology" that Alex refined to a high art and that have been so highly successful in assessment and control of various diseases appear to me to be applicable to the medical care process itself. My life has been enriched by having known Alex and having had him as a friend, and I hope that his memory is properly served by this volume.

The authors of the chapters all collaborated eagerly. In addition, I would like to thank the following members of the American College of Physician Executives who graciously served as chapter reviewers: John Bauers, Donald Blanford, Mark Bloomberg, Lowell Butman, Leslie Cashel, Alan Chernov, R. William Corwin, Clara Ersoz, Attilio Granata, J. Jerome Cohen, Cary Gutbezahl, Roger Hand, Jonathan Harding, James Hoffman, Charles Hollerman, H. D. Kerman, Paul LaMarche, Barbara LeTourneau, Henry Liss, Charles Massaro, Michael McGarvey, Kathleen Musser, Lee Newcomer, Clifford Ossorio, Carl Phipps, David Posner, Stephen Shultz, Alan Smith, Richard Somma, Morris Spierer, Loren Vorlicky, Jerrold Weinberg, Bruce Weiss, Michael Werdmann, and Harry Wetzler.

I am grateful to Claudette Levesque, my administrative assistant in the Medical Director's Office of Harvard Community Health Plan of New England, who coordinated the many details involved in getting the materials together from the authors and reviewers, and to Wes Curry in the offices of the American College of Physician Executives, who applied his editorial skills to the manuscripts.

Finally, and most important, I am indebted to Sylvia, who has put up with my many extracurricular activities, including this book. She, Amy, and Abby, by their love, give me the optimism to think that it is worth applying oneself to difficult problems and that by doing so we can make the world a better place in which to live.—*Stephen C. Schoenbaum, MD, MPH, Providence, R.I., September 30, 1995.*

INTRODUCTION

There are many in health care who think that quality improvement was a fad of the late 1980s. Although in the mid-1990s fewer institutions may be setting up or continuing to run courses based on the works of Deming and Juran, or talking about quality circles, or simultaneously chartering and running dozens of specifically designated "quality" project teams, an argument can be made that not only is quality management going strong in health care but it is gaining momentum. In large part this is due to the fact that more measurement of performance is being done. Because of this we are discovering room for improvement of care; and, pari passu, quality of health care is less universally accepted as a given. Most important, whether the work is done by quality improvement teams, plain old project teams, or just as part of "daily work life," there is now a significant amount of substantive work going on to improve the deficiencies in care that have been and are being identified.

Measurement literally drives quality improvement. It provides the energy that propels a manager around the quality management cycle. If you think about it, you will find that measurement plays at least four critical roles in driving quality improvement:

▌ It provides information that allows managers to set goals for improvement.

▌ It tells managers what care processes are already in place.

▌ It tells managers whether the implementation steps they have taken to improve a process have actually led to an improved process.

▌ It tells managers whether the processes they have implemented are achieving the outcomes they desired.

No single type of measurement, e.g., process or outcome, can provide all the information managers need. Measurement, per se, is important.

This monograph aims to provide physician executives with information about measurement. It is not a book on how to measure. Rather, it consists of a series of essays on aspects of measurement. These essays have been designed to be relatively short and, ideally, readable. The idea was to produce a set of pieces that would help physician executives understand the context in which measurement of health care must occur and to give physician executives an understanding of the issues that must be dealt with in managing the process of measuring clinical care. The essays need not be read in sequence.

There are three sections to the monograph: The first has been written by persons who all have a deep interest in health care and health care quality, but who represent very different perspectives on health care, including those of purchasers, consumers, clinicians, and managers. The authors have tried to explain what they are looking for from measurements of care—what they need, what they have, and what they do not yet have. An interesting fact one derives from reading this series of essays is the degree of overlap of needs and desires for information among persons with such different perspectives. This is an important realization for executives, because it suggests that, although the possibilities for measurement may be virtually infinite, there is a core area of overlapping customer needs that merits top priority for design of measurements and design of systems to make it easier to do the measurements.

The second section of the monograph, without being technical, addresses a few of the important technical considerations in measurement. These include: adjustment for case mix, severity-of-illness, or risk—a critical issue if one is to compare outcomes measurements across providers or health care systems; obtaining information directly from patients, as in surveys or patient reports; feedback of performance data, an act that turns out to play a key role in stimulating performance improvement; and developing sophisticated experimental designs so that limited amounts of measurement information can provide maximum improvements in care.

The final section of the monograph addresses several topical issues for executives. It includes: a mini-symposium with three different essays or viewpoints on the issue of whether measurement of clinical performance should be linked to compensation; an essay on linking measurement to clinical guidelines; a piece on the issue of shared decision making, a technique in which outcomes measurements are presented to patients to help them make important decisions about their care in concert with their clinician; and an essay on outcomes measurement itself—what it is, and what it is not.

Anyone who trained in medicine prior to the past decade heard relatively little about measurement of care. Most training was oriented toward individual cases. To the extent that the medical curriculum included any study of epidemiology, the material presented was usually about communicable disease epidemics or, possibly, about how to read the literature critically. While these areas remain important, health care has broader dimensions. One can apply measurement methods not just to the occurrence of disease or to clinical trials but to the nature of the structure, processes, and outcomes of the health care system itself. Just as understanding the nature of individual clinical cases or the patterns of occurrence of disease has led to improvements in the way physicians approach clinical care, an understanding of our processes and outcomes of care will improve the entire care system. Executives, who play a vital role in the management of that system, need to understand what they can learn from well-designed measurements and need to manage the measurement process itself within their institutions. It is hoped that this monograph will provide some perspective to enable executives to carry out this part of their jobs better.

Stephen C. Schoenbaum, MD, MPH
Providence, R.I.
September 30, 1995

CONTENTS

SECTION I. PERSPECTIVES ON MEASUREMENTS OF CLINICAL CARE

SECTION II. TECHNICAL CONSIDERATIONS IN MEASUREMENT OF CLINICAL CARE

SECTION III. TOPICAL ISSUES

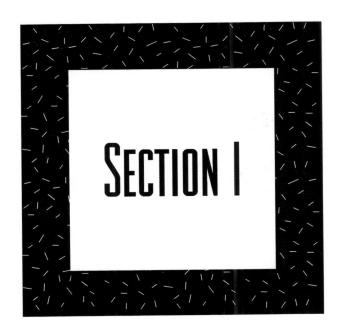

Section I

Perspectives on Measurements of Clinical Care

CHAPTER 1

What Information Would Purchasers Like to See?

by Helen Darling

Employers and other purchasers want information from health plans to assess health plan performance, determine the "value" they are obtaining for their investment, permit dialogue with health plans concerning performance, and promote continuous quality improvement. Employers also want to provide selected information to their employees so they can make the most appropriate decisions for themselves and their families.

Employers/purchasers want health plans to have useful, comparable data and information so that the health plans can judge their own performance against benchmark delivery systems. In the future, we hope to develop compendia of optimal performance standards and identify "best practices" related to the most efficient and effective performance. Plans might then adopt practices that produce the best outcomes. Purchasers could also reward health plans with the best performance by sharing information on them, by favored pricing, and by positive publicity.

At this early stage, the measures and data systems under development in health plans will be most useful in *beginning* dialogues between the plans and purchasers to communicate what directions purchasers find important. Information should help point to clinical or management areas for further study or improvement. As described by Janet Corrigan in Chapter 5, a group of employers and plans worked for more than 20 months to develop common data sets and standard definitions and methodology for reporting (the HEDIS instrument). We, at Xerox, do not believe that the numbers will mirror exactly the underlying reality we want to measure, but the data will help identify subjects for further study and give directionally accurate, "ballpark" estimates of health plan performance. For example, in 1993, in reports obtained from HMOs across the country, statistics on percentages of women who received mammograms within the prior two years ranged from a low of 35 to 73 percent. All of our HMOs had rates far below the optimal. We have no way of knowing if any or all of the rates reflect reality, although we hope the higher rates are the more accurate ones and low rates are due to poor record-keeping. But each HMO's rate can and should be improved. All will get much better at reporting and recording tests and treatments. Complete, accurate recording is of key importance to good patient care. We also know health plans will pay a lot more attention to providing mammograms by seeing comparative data (See Chapter 12). Soon, we would hope to obtain measurements of the stage of detection of breast cancer so we will learn more about the combined effects in HMOs of screening, appropriate follow-ups, high risk identification, breast exams, etc. The earlier we refine the measurement systems we need, the sooner we will be able to measure accurately the quality, cost, effectiveness, appropriateness, and efficacy of the delivery of health care to our employees and their families, as well as the public-at-large.

Background

The reader may reasonably wonder why large employers and other purchasers are spending so much time and money on topics not directly related to their core businesses. Until the early 1980s, employers and other purchasers of health care were willing to accept the idea that health care treatment decisions, including what would be reimbursed by employers and other third-party payers, were concerns that only physicians and other health professionals could understand or influence. Indeed, many business executives felt, and today still feel, that management of the health system should be left to physicians, other clinicians, health administrators, and the army of specialists who operate the highly complex institutions that constitute today's health system. Such purchasers— the hands-off managers—have typically sent signals to the health system based on the prices they were willing to pay or able to pay. They began cutting back on what they would pay for, although, even with reduced coverage, the rate of growth in medical claims expenses remained in the double-digit, sometimes high double-digit, range. These purchasers offered an indemnity-type, fee-for-service plan, usually self-insured, and, perhaps, one or more managed care options. The managed care options were not favorably priced to the employee unless the employer enjoyed considerable savings, although the indemnity plan usually had substantial cost-sharing (e.g., increased deductibles and copayments) for the employee and a number of limits on coverage. (e.g., $1 million lifetime limit or $50,000 limit on mental health and substance abuse.) These purchasers were the ones that physicians, administrators, and health plan managers believe were concerned only with costs.

By the early to mid-1980s, some large employers, including Xerox, Digital Equipment, and General Electric, that had comprehensive health benefits and modest cost-sharing concluded that reducing the level of reimbursement and what the company would pay for would leave their employees exposed to high medical costs. There was particular concern for employees with young families, who tended to be at the lower end of the pay scales and mostly healthy. For them, the typical indemnity-type coverage paid for little unless they were very sick. They then had high out-of-pocket costs. Many of the well-child, preventive services needed by their families were not covered.

Equally as disturbing for these large employers was the conclusion that maintaining the traditional insurance-type program would continue to support a medical care system that was providing more and more services and ever more expensive acute medical/surgical treatment without concomitant improvements in the overall health of their employees. Put another way, we were spending a growing share of our corporate and national resources on treatments that were not producing as much health as the investment should have produced. For example, average cost of family coverage in fee-for-service is $10,000. As a consequence, many of the largest purchasers, including Xerox, Digital, GTE, GE, PepsiCo, Honeywell, Marriott, Southwestern Bell, Ameritech, and Southern California Edison, to name only a few, have moved from a passive bill-paying roll to a more activist role aimed at developing health delivery systems that are organized to produce more actual "health " for the investment. This includes work with patients to make changes in life-style and behavior that we know can make measurable differences in the length and quality of people's lives.

Why Not Let the Health System Reform Itself?

Purchasers have lost patience with systems that continue to consume health care dollars at rates far above the employers' abilities to produce the net revenues needed to pay for that care. In short, employers cannot wait for health system providers to understand how serious employers' financial situation is. Private employers are reeling from world-wide recession and the loss of manufacturing jobs because U.S. firms are not competitive in a global economy. Public-sector employers are facing balking taxpayers who will not continue to pay ever higher costs for high labor costs exacerbated by comprehensive medical coverage that public employees enjoy. Instead, the largest employers have become more demanding "as customers," more insistent on paying for what they believe will make a measurable difference in health outcomes, and not paying for inefficient systems and unnecessary, inappropriate, or less than optimal services.

Although savvy purchasers know that we are a long way from having all of the science-based knowledge that we need to continually make the best medical and health promotion decisions, we already know a lot more than we apply systematically. Purchasers have become convinced that progress will be made most rapidly if they pressure health plans to spend time on health-enhancing activities, some of which may be delivered more cost-effectively by nonphysician providers. We know that physicians can have substantial influence on their patients on behaviors such as smoking; yet they do not always counsel their patients to the extent they could and should. Many purchasers believe physicians should be more active counselors concerning health, and they should use nonphysicians to spend time with patients to ensure they get all of their questions answered, understand, and are motivated to comply with doctors' recommended treatments.

Do HMOs "Cream-Skim?" Do Employers Overpay HMOs or Other Capitated Plans?

Traditionally, employers, especially very large employers, have been skeptical about HMOs. They believed that younger, healthier employees tend to select HMOs, while older, sicker employees tend to remain in their indemnity plans. Because large employers typically have been "self-insured," each year the costs of the fee-for-service plan increased and each year a progressively sicker population or a population of higher users of the medical benefits would stay. (In the insurance world, this is called the "death spiral.")

We, at Xerox, believe that the behavior of employees and the consequence of annual health plan selections are more complicated than the simpler models have described, but our fee-for-service plan's enrollees do have a significantly higher "burden of illness"—as measured by the New England Medical Center-administered "Employee

Health Care Value Survey." The availability and reporting of HEDIS data (see below and Chapter 5) will settle some of the long-standing questions concerning the selection patterns of the relatively healthy and relatively sicker and older employees. For example, there will be data on the extensive areas (e.g., mental health and substance abuse) that HMOs have been least likely to cover extensively. In time, appropriate and equitable adjustments in premiums can be developed and used. We want to provide fair payments on a prepaid, capitated basis. Eventually, we would like to have sound methods of risk adjustment (see Chapter 10) to ensure that there are no financial disincentives to care for the people who can most benefit from well-coordinated care—that is, patients with serious acute or chronic problems.

In prepaid capitated payment environments, employers are concerned that they are paying for services in advance with little or no certainty that their employees will get the services paid for. Some employers have dealt with this problem by encouraging employees to join HMOs but insisting on an arrangement in which the employers only pay for services rendered ("self-insured" managed care.) Employers are buying into a more efficient service delivery system, but they are buying only the services that their employees obtain. Many employers and consultants will argue that this kind of self-insured managed care arrangement is the least expensive and, perhaps, most cost-effective for employers.

Another approach—the one that Xerox has chosen—is based on the belief that the company should help employees select HMOs that are true *systems* of care. These systems must be organized to be responsible for each member's health. They must identify important, manageable risk factors, and they must identify problems when it is possible to intervene successfully. Once an employer decides that it is a good idea to buy into systems of care organized for disease/injury prevention, health promotion, and delivering high-quality care for illnesses, the employer will also want proof that such services are being provided and that they are being provided in the most cost-efficient manner. Although some of the best known HMOs do routinely make available their own statistics, many do not. It is clear that the failure of some HMOs to moderate their increases in health premiums is not solely due to forces beyond the plan's control (as some plans argue). For example, very loosely managed IPA-model HMOs sometimes have a hard time controlling annual premium costs. They will tell purchasers and regulators that their high costs are due to hospital price increases or other factors beyond their control. Yet, when the data are available, such HMOs often have high use of emergency departments and elevated levels of inpatient admissions and patient days. Put another way, they are, in fact, not really "managing " utilization. This is not an uncommon problem, especially in immature HMO markets where there have been few pressures to do much more than be slightly more efficient than the fee-for-service system.

What Specific Data Do Purchasers Want?

Because purchasers want to make available and encourage their employees to select the more efficient and effective health care systems, they want information from their plans that will document that they are more efficient and effective.

The list of data and indicators that purchasers want can be categorized broadly by type. In general, employer/purchasers are concerned with:

- Quality of care
- Financial control, stability, and solvency
- Utilization
- Access and network/staff adequacy
- Member satisfaction
- Problem resolution

For each category, the reasons for wanting data and documentation apply throughout. Broadly, the reasons can be characterized as accountability to the purchaser and members and can be listed as a set of questions:

- Are we getting what we think we are paying for?
- Are we paying for what we want to be paying for?
- Is the health plan delivering what it thinks it is delivering?
- Is the health plan providing the services that it wants to be providing?
- Is the health plan producing services in the most efficient and effective way?
- Is the health plan providing services in a manner that is superior to those of other similarly positioned health plans with roughly similar populations?
- How does the health plan perform against the benchmark or the gold standard in each area?
- What changes need to be made in order to improve performance in these areas?

Documentation Based on Comparable Data
The rationale for most of the indicators on utilization is pretty self-evident. For example, utilization of hospital resources can be very expensive. Management of hospital utilization is essential if the health plan is to remain solvent and have the resources to provide other needed services.

Total Quality Management
All of the data listed above are essential to engage in total quality management—a method of ensuring quality of care. Employers are much more interested in improvement of care than in the "inspection/policing" roles of traditional quality assurance programs, such as the federal PRO program.

We Don't Manage What We Don't Measure
Essential to total quality management is the belief that activities and results that are not measured are also not likely to be managed and delivered properly or systematically. For example, a study of cervical cancer screening in a large HMO, which is devoted to doing such screenings, found that a significant number of women at possible risk were not

getting screened, a significant number of the test results were not being reported back and being incorporated in the medical record, and appropriate follow-up was not taking place when it should have.* When the plan began measuring and reporting on cervical cancer screening, it learned that procedures that everyone thought were routine were not routine. It needed to design and implement quality improvement to do what it wanted to do in the first place—screen effectively and efficiently for cervical cancer.

Quality of Care

Measures of quality of care themselves can be improved. They tend to reflect process or structural measures, rather than the outcomes of treatment that we would all like to measure. But we believe we have to start with the measures we have in HEDIS 2.0/2.5 today for several reasons. We know the best measures are those that document outcomes. (Is a patient walking without pain or limitations after a hip replacement operation? Is a patient free of debilitating, crippling anxieties and severe depression?) We do not yet routinely have available the measures of these outcomes. Progress has been made in the past few years, and, increasingly, research studies are incorporating instruments measuring outcomes such as the so-called SF 36 (Short Form 36 item instrument measuring health status, which can be used at various stages of treatment). Until rigorous assessments of all treatment results are routinely included, we will need to obtain data on the processes or activities of treatment and use those as proxies for outcomes. In addition, obtaining data on treatment allows the analyst to identify the possible problem or system failure driving the particular result. Even when we have outcomes data, we will need to know something about the structure and organization of care to know what contributed to the result and what should be changed.

Health Plans Need Data on All Services

In order to provide the comprehensive data set, health plans will need extensive, high-quality data from *all sites* of care. Employers expect health plans to manage well all aspects of health care, including being certain that the health plans are using the best hospitals, diagnostic testing, and surgery centers. As the demand for accountability increases for health plans, they will in turn pressure hospitals, physician groups, and other suppliers to be better, more cost-effective, more attentive to customer satisfaction, and more willing to document all they are doing on a timely basis.

Access

One of the areas of greatest controversy for employers and their employees, especially those that are very new to any form of "managed care," is referred to as "access." This often means something different to employees than to health care professionals. To employees, this means can they get to a doctor of their choice when they want or need one. Xerox looks very carefully at the number and percentage of primary care physicians accepting new patients. As far as we are concerned , it should be 100 percent or close to it. We have found that employees feel that their *effective* access is restrained and their

---

* Schoenbaum, S., and Gottlieb, L. "Algorithm Based Improvement of Clinical Quality." *British Medical Journal* 301:1374-6, Dec. 15, 1990.

choices nonexistent if there are only a few physicians in a geographic area with open practices. IPA-HMO directories often list doctors by large communities, which may not track to commuter patterns, shopping patterns, etc. What may look like a reasonable number of doctors in a large area may not be a reasonable number when examined through employees' eyes.

Is There Outreach to New/Nonusing Members?

Employers, including Xerox, want to be sure that the HMO is doing a good job of reaching out to members who are not using the health plan. While we are not interested in making work or arguing for the old "annual" check-up, the HMOs should make an aggressive effort to make sure every new member is persuasively counseled to visit his or her primary care practitioner at least once to discuss possible risk factors, including how they might affect an individual over time, and to conduct age/gender/risk-appropriate examinations and screening tests. At that visit, the primary care provider should discuss the kinds of life-style changes that contribute to improved health.

We recognize that the HMO cannot force a member to come in, but we are convinced that the potential value of such visits, given how many people have undetected problems such as hypertension and depression, is great. We believe that such visits might prevent some serious, costly illness later. If we did not believe in this risk identification, health promotion, and maintenance model of health care, we could actually save money by not using HMOs for our "healthy," low-user employees. By requiring that HMOs identify and measure those adults who have not had meaningful contact with a primary care provider within the prior three years, we know that we are pushing HMOs to work to "maintain health." Also, we do not consider it unreasonable, since we pay about $200 a month for an individual. For someone who has not been seen even once in three years, we would have spent approximately $7,200 and received, perhaps, no service for that payment.

Member Satisfaction

Xerox considers the measurement of member or "customer" satisfaction as central to all that we are trying to achieve. Measurement must be systematized and done on the basis of high-quality instruments, proper sampling, reliable response rates, and statistically rigorous objective analysis. Employees select their plans on an annual basis, along with other objective information, including accreditation by the National Committee for Quality Assurance (NCQA.) Employees need to know which plans have high proportions of "very satisfied" members and which do not before they lock themselves into a yearlong commitment. Turnover of patients plays havoc with people's lives, breaks continuity of care, and is very expensive to the plans and patients. The more we can learn about areas of dissatisfaction, the more we can avoid costly disenrollments and the better we can create satisfied members.

In summary, Xerox is most interested in the development of a measurement system that will produce information about health plan performance to:

■ Advance what we know about what works effectively in the daily practice of medicine in organized delivery systems, such as HMOs.

- Assist in improving performance (continuous quality improvement) in all areas—prevention and health maintenance, clinical practice and outcomes of treatment, administration and management, member and patient satisfaction, and moderation of cost increases.

- Continue an ongoing dialogue between health plans and purchasers concerning the strategic directions of the health plans and their cosuppliers (hospitals, physicians, etc.)

- Share selected data with employees to assist them in making their annual health plan choices.

In all instances, Xerox works in a partnership with health plans to sharply improve the quality and appropriateness of health care delivered to its employees and their families. By showcasing and rewarding outstanding performance and "best practices," we are convinced that we will all benefit, along with the public-at-large.

CHAPTER 2

Employers' Need for Clinical Data in Managing Health Care Costs

by Dwight N. McNeill and Bruce E. Bradley, MBA

Employers did not take health care costs seriously until the 1980s. Up to that time, it was basically a personnel function of paying the premiums and increasing benefits to stay competitive in recruiting staff. Health care costs for employers rose in the '80s in double-digit percentages year after year and earned a place at the boardroom table as a major cost center in need of control. Automakers complained that their single most expensive supplier cost in manufacturing a car was health care, above that of the largest supplier of steel. In fact, by the early '90s, health care costs consumed 50 percent of corporate after-tax profits.

GTE, like other major corporations, developed strategic initiatives to harness the problem and bring it under control. GTE decided to attack the problem by managing health care as it would any of its other lines of business by applying principles and practices of value-based purchasing, reengineering, and total quality management. Indeed, health care costs GTE about $700 million per year, which is equivalent to the revenues of an average Fortune 500 company. Its senior management approved a strategic comprehensive health care cost containment program in 1991 and hired staff to manage health care benefits and programs on a day-to-day basis.

Two key tactics related to data collection were to provide incentives for employees to select the most cost-effective managed care plans and to develop a state-of-the-art, integrated information system that tracks and reports on all health-related activities, ranging from cost and utilization, to quality and outcomes, to patient satisfaction.

Early Corporate Cost Containment Data

Corporations initially measured items that were available and feasible but were not necessarily the measures needed to ascertain quality and cost-effectiveness of health care organizations. This approach runs counter to Peter Drucker's dictum that the most dangerous thing in the world is the right answer to the wrong question. Claims data from indemnity insurance carriers became a prime source of data for cost containment analyses. Most of the focus initially was (and still is) on cost and related elements of unit price and utilization of services. The analytic approach was to explore the data for variations among groups, or from norms, or from benchmark levels. This variation approach was pioneered by Wennberg and others at the Dartmouth Medical School with studies of widely varying rates of tonsillectomy in New England. It raised the question that, if the incidence of disease is not variable, why is medical practice so different? Hence, issues of quality, physician practice patterns, and unnecessary utilization could be forced to the surface for more scrutiny.

One example of the claims/variation analysis approach to health care cost containment comes from the mental health area. Mental health costs reportedly increased at an average of 47 percent for large employers in 1987.* This increase was not predicted, was startlingly high, and was way out of line with other medical cost increases. Variation analyses by payers on price and use yielded widely varying patterns of utilization, including very long lengths of stay for adolescents and unusually high costs for private hospitals. Also, mental health diagnoses, such as psychoses and neuroses, rose to the top of high-cost diagnoses lists as reported in standard reports from emerging cost containment reporting software. Although there was some attempt to demonstrate cost-effective outcomes for treatments by providers, there was an overwhelming rising tide to reduce corporate liability in areas that were questionable. These data provided "low hanging fruit" that were "easy pickings" for cost cutting. The variation approach was simply too potent. The political times (the uncompassionate Reagan years) and the corporate times (recession, global competition, and downsizing), which demanded any and all cost reductions to save the company, enabled these relatively incomplete data approaches to be influential in persuading some benefit managers to slash benefits and others to implement "carve-out" managed mental health care.

Making decisions based on only part of the equation (costs and not quality) resulted in readily achievable and significant gains in mental health in particular and in health care in general. Prices were reduced, utilization was lowered, networks of efficient providers were formed, and the health care cost trend was reduced to single digits for the first time in a decade by 1992.

But times are changing, and there is much more interest on the part of employers in quality and clinical information at this time because of the following factors:

■ Employers believe they have been successful in moderating health care costs. Indeed, overall managed care premium increases for GTE averaged less than 1 percent in 1995, following a 3.5 percent increase in 1994. Employers are drawing upon other business skills to apply to health care management, including reengineering, asset (human) management, supplier management, and occupational medicine.

■ Marketplace competition requires more information about quality and cost in order for consumers to make decisions based on value. These decisions, in turn, will drive health care organizations to improve quality and efficiency.

---

* Foster Higgins, 1990, *Report on Mental Health and Substance Abuse Methods*, p. 6.

Measuring Clinical Care: A Guide for Physician Executives

- There is recognition that an expanded view of health preservation is needed in order to solve the longer term issues of decreasing the incidence of illness. This includes placing more emphasis on life-style management, early intervention, and other public health prevention principles.

- There is evidence that one can pay less and get more (quality) in health care, e.g., with centers of excellence performing high-volume procedures such as coronary bypass. GTE data show that health plans in the 90th percentile and above on overall quality measures have a significantly lower cost trend than health plans of lesser quality. Because an emphasis on quality drives down cost, more focus and effort should be directed upstream at the factors causing high costs. This often involves reengineering clinical care processes.

- The quality movement (CQI, TQM) has led to an emphasis on three things— "quality is job 1," "no rejects," and "do it right the first time." It has transformed many American industries, such as automakers. Employers want to transfer these proven business skills in their own industries to the business of health care management in order to achieve quantum leaps in quality improvement.

- Consumerism, downsizing, and employee empowerment are converging forces that lay the groundwork for more employee decision making about the selection of their health plans. This will include providing more information to employees about health plan performance. Incremental value must be demonstrated to employees in order for them to keep and/or to switch plans. As competition on price gets more intense and more homogeneous, there will be a focus on quality as the discriminating feature between plans.

- Employers have a genuine concern for their employees' welfare and view the provision of high-quality health care benefits as a corporate responsibility.

- The lean human resource function of corporations in the '90s cannot accommodate/respond to high levels of employee "noise" caused by complaints about poorly performing plans. Hence, the need for efficiency of administration also fosters the need for high-quality plans.

GTE's Approach to Value Measurement

GTE has developed a framework to measure overall value of a plan, as illustrated in figure 1, page 12.

- **Cost.** This area includes measures of efficiency, including utilization, unit price, premiums, and administrative costs.

- **Benefit level.** GTE developed a standard benefit plan for HMOs and Point of Service (POS) plans. The benefit design for indemnity and POS plans compared to HMOs is different and requires that the plans be standardized on the amount of

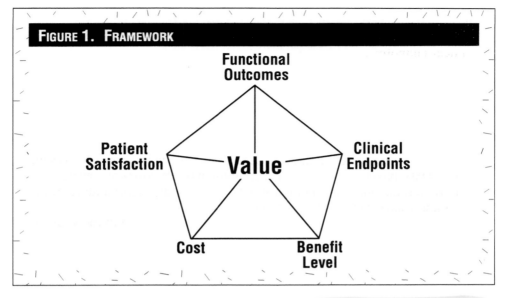

FIGURE 1. FRAMEWORK

Functional
Outcomes

Patient
Satisfaction

Value

Clinical
Endpoints

Cost

Benefit
Level

benefit provided. On average, our HMO standard benefit design provides a benefit level that is 14 percent richer than that of the indemnity plan in terms of more benefits covered and lower deductibles and copayments. So, in quantifying value, differences in benefit level need to be taken into account.

- **Patient satisfaction.** What the employee thinks about access, communications, paperwork, quality of care, etc. are all important inputs to understanding the consumer's perspective as a dimension of quality.

- **Functional outcomes.** These are measures of the functioning of the members of the population, including such things as physical and mental functioning, pain and vitality, role limitations, and quality of life. This is at the apex of the pentagon, because it is the most important quality issue, i.e., are persons functioning well as a result of their health management?

- **Clinical endpoints.** Are preferred practice patterns being observed for selected conditions? Is serious disease being detected early? Are certain condition-specific outcomes being achieved?

The measurement tools that GTE uses for each of these areas are (figure 2, page 13):

- **Patient satisfaction/functional outcomes.** These measures are obtained from the Employee Health Care Value Survey, which was conducted by the Health Institute of the New England Medical Center in Boston, Mass., on behalf of a consortium of employers, including Digital, GTE, and Xerox. The survey included over 25,000 employees in 6 major health care markets, including 32 plans. Instruments in the survey included the GHAA patient satisfaction instrument, the SF-36, items from the Medical Outcomes Study on chronic disease, and health risk assessment items from the Carter Center for Disease Prevention. The survey data on health burden will also contribute to better risk adjustment of plans when making plan comparisons.

■ **Clinical endpoints.** Some of these quality measures are from HEDIS 2.0/2.5 (see Chapter 5) and include childhood immunization, cholesterol screening, mammography screening, cervical cancer screening, low-birthweight deliveries, prenatal care in first trimester, asthma inpatient admission rates, diabetic retinal exams, and ambulatory follow-up for affective disorders. HEDIS is a multiconstituency effort between health plans and employers, under the umbrella of the National Committee for Quality Assurance, to develop a core set of performance measures for health plan reporting. Another source of clinical endpoint data is the Outcomes Management System (OMS) project, the product of a consortium of employers and managed care organizations that looks at condition-specific outcomes and general functional outcomes and relates them to clinical guidelines. The strength of the OMS is in complementing patient-reported functional outcome data (derived from the SF-36) with specific questions that provide clinical insight as to why the patient is feeling bad. For example, for a patient with diabetes, the functional outcome measures can detect that the patient does not feel good, but a more specific measure is needed to ascertain whether the ill feeling is due to an improper insulin dose, peripheral neuropathy, or diabetic retinopathy. It should be noted that the performance of health care organizations is kept confidential at this time in order to foster collaboration rather than competition among organizations.

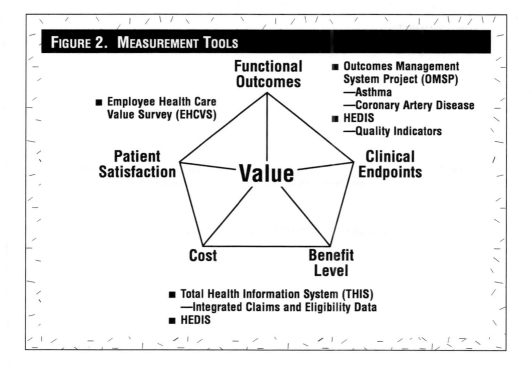

FIGURE 2. MEASUREMENT TOOLS

Functional Outcomes

■ Outcomes Management System Project (OMSP)
—Asthma
—Coronary Artery Disease
■ HEDIS
—Quality Indicators

■ Employee Health Care Value Survey (EHCVS)

Patient Satisfaction

Value

Clinical Endpoints

Cost

Benefit Level

■ Total Health Information System (THIS)
—Integrated Claims and Eligibility Data
■ HEDIS

- **Cost.** GTE has developed an integrated health care information system that captures use and price and eligibility information for all health care programs and integrates information from other sources, including HEDIS and the Value Survey, so that all information on a given plan is accessible through an on-line system.

What's next in clinical data collection by large employers:

- **Prevention/life-style management.** A strategy that is gaining momentum with employers is reduction in the demand for services so that the costs incurred in the supply of services will be dramatically reduced. GTE spends a conservative $60 million per year on preventable life-style illnesses, including those caused by tobacco and alcohol use, sedentary life-style, fatty diet, etc. The information needed here includes risk assessment data, clinical history, program utilization data, and follow-up data. Many employers are overcoming the perceived confidentiality problem of collecting and using these data through expert communication of intent about partnership between the employer and the employee, through financial incentives, and by making the program voluntary.

- **Consumer measures of health status and functional outcomes** should become a vital statistic that is collected routinely, risk adjusted, and compared plan to plan. This should be reported by the plans as a part of future editions of HEDIS. Ideally, the data would be collected by a national survey research firm that would use standard methods across all health plans.

- **Patient-centered measures of satisfaction and evaluations of plans** will become routine and be done by a third party.

- **Risk-adjustment data and methods** will be needed to equalize health plans on the basis of types of patients, severity, complexity, and health burden so that fair comparisons can be made between the plans on performance measures.

- **Risk sharing on quality and outcomes.** If we set performance targets based on length of stay or hospital admission rate, why can't we do the same for preventable admissions, level of functioning for chronic diseases, or a "health index" for the enrollee population? This has more to do with leadership than with financial arrangements. Metrics tend to become targets, and financial underpinnings tend to concentrate attention. Employers want the focus on quality and outcomes, and performance contracts have worked well for them.

- **Use of clinical data by multiple constituencies.** Much of the change in health care delivery happens because doctors change behavior, to some extent on the basis of feedback of clinical data. However, as figure 3, page 15, shows, there are many uses of clinical data by employers and employees. GTE has used quality data for pricing health plans to provide incentives for employees to select the most cost-effective plan, for consumer reports with health plan performance ratings to provide information to employees to enable them to make value-based purchasing decisions, and for quality leadership and continuous quality improvement processes with the plans.

Are Corporations Too Involved with Medical Measurement?

Employers have had to fight hard and to pay dearly for information about health plan performance. In order to manage performance, they have to measure it. What they measure should be not only cost-based, but overall performance-based. In health care, that involves the outcomes of services, and the outcomes of services are intimately involved with the clinical practice of medicine. Health plans have not been forthcoming in providing information for employers in the past. Today, however, most employers are insisting on HEDIS reporting, and many will freeze enrollment in a plan if it is not provided. And the demands for more and better data on quality and outcomes will continue.

The evolution of employers' management of health care is displayed in figure 4, below. As indicated earlier, employers' involvement with health care up until the

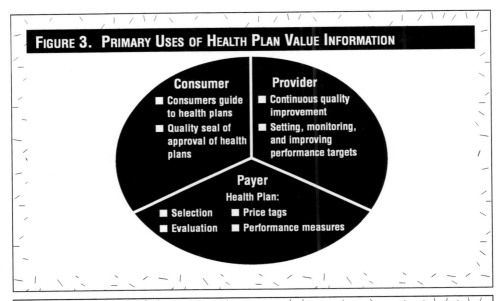

FIGURE 3. PRIMARY USES OF HEALTH PLAN VALUE INFORMATION

Consumer
- Consumers guide to health plans
- Quality seal of approval of health plans

Provider
- Continuous quality improvement
- Setting, monitoring, and improving performance targets

Payer
Health Plan:
- Selection
- Price tags
- Evaluation
- Performance measures

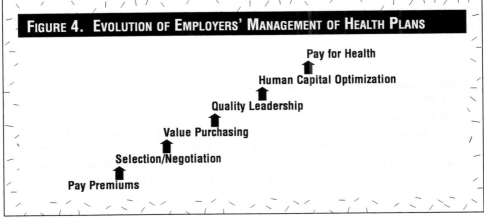

FIGURE 4. EVOLUTION OF EMPLOYERS' MANAGEMENT OF HEALTH PLANS

Pay for Health

Human Capital Optimization

Quality Leadership

Value Purchasing

Selection/Negotiation

Pay Premiums

mid-'80s was primarily to pay the premiums, just as they would do with other routine supplier charges. During the 1980s, however, the cost of health care began to increase at alarming rates, year after year. Managed care was beginning to be seen as an alternative to traditional indemnity plans. Both of these forces caused employers to think about selecting alternative plans. In addition to selection of plans, employers got into the business of managing the price of plans by negotiating premiums, just as they would any other supplier's quote and proposal.

It then became apparent that plans had different premiums and different rates of increase. An employer could deal with plans individually, but employers again preferred to apply a well-honed business principle, value purchasing. This required performance measures in addition to simple cost measures. At first, the performance measures were price- and utilization-based. HEDIS evolved out of the need for a more expanded set of routinely available performance measures. Value purchasing fits into the theme of managed competition, where consumers have information on quality and cost and make decisions based on overall value. The value purchasing stage of development is where most enlightened employers are today.

We see the following as future directions that employers will move toward as they seek to improve their management of health plans:

- **Quality Leadership.** Employers were influential and insistent that plans provide performance data through HEDIS. Now that HEDIS data and other data are available to employers, how will they be used? In addition to pricing and consumer guides, GTE will use the information to focus on quality. Internal studies of plans show that quality is related to lower cost trends and, over time, to lower premium costs. GTE believes that quality is the main driver for cost control and needs to be the primary focus. A focus on costs alone can only provide incremental savings. A focus on quality can take out huge chunks of costs by the reengineering of processes. GTE has taken a quality leadership role to convene forums with our plans; provide feedback from the data; focus on the critical areas for improvement; monitor results; and, in general, emphasize quality as what matters to GTE for managing health care. Hence, this process is more than providing data on actual versus benchmarks, more than saying there is variation, so do something about it. It involves deciding what matters to GTE and developing a campaign to improve quality and ultimately health.

- **Human Capital Optimization.** We need to move beyond medical management. This focus on the component parts of the overall health of the individual limits benefits that can derive from integration of all health care, such as disability, worker's compensation, and community factors related to health and illness. We need to focus on human capital optimization. All of the assets of the individual need to be managed to drive toward maximal productivity, for the good of the individual and the good of the corporation. Some would say that health-related costs are the largest detractor from productivity. One's health needs to be viewed as an asset, as are skill sets, motivation, and organizational focus. HMOs have done a good job in integrating the health needs of the individual and in taking financial responsibility for the full vertical management of needs. We need to broaden that "sand-box" to include coordination across health care systems, a more determined effort to preserve health,

Measuring Clinical Care: A Guide for Physician Executives

and consortiums of plans and community resources to improve health conditions of the community the plans serve.

■ **Pay for Health.** Metrics oftentimes define targets. Our goals become operationalized by our ability to measure them. Our focus on health care has led to metrics about cost of care, large case costs, utilization, PMPM, etc. The ultimate goal of a plan is too achieve the highest possible health status for its population of members. Rather than concentrating on PMPM (per member per month costs), we need to look at HIM (Health Index of Membership). Rather than LOS (length of stay), we need FIR (Functional Improvement Rates). Perhaps the most important feature of the Value Survey work has been the measurement of health status and functional status. These data can be the foundation for a focus on health or "health leadership." There are financial arrangements in business and in health care that provide incentives for performance. Most of these measures have to do with costs. For example, a vendor may receive more or less of an administrative fee if certain financial targets are met, e.g. the PMPM for mental health. Performance targets are powerful tools for focusing attention, and employers will want to use them for a focus on health.

CHAPTER 3

What Information Would Consumers Like to See?

by Roberta N. Clark, PhD, MBA

We can best characterize the making of health care provider selection decisions by many consumers in one of two ways: "the blind leading the blind" or "operating without a compass." A study for Children's Hospital in Boston a number of years ago found that people new to a neighborhood would often choose a pediatrician by asking their new neighbors whom they would recommend; most often, the neighbors recommended their own pediatrician because they knew little about other pediatricians. Another source of information used by people new to the neighborhood was the local emergency department (when a health need first arose), from which they might then receive a referral to a local physician; or they would turn to that source of all knowledge, the *Yellow Pages* and, not unlike a child playing "pin the tail on the donkey," figuratively close their eyes and select a physician, with little to guide them other than the physician's address, telephone number, and listed specialty.[1]

There has been a marginal increase in the amount of information on physicians available to consumers; however, much of it is biased toward serving the interests of the information provider. "Ask a Nurse" and physician referral programs are usually sponsored by a specific hospital or set of hospitals with the purpose of promoting their own physicians, the premise being the more patients a hospital feeds its physicians, the more patients the physician admits to that hospital.

Some consumers, empowered by consumer groups such as the People's Medical Society, a national organization whose membership is well over 100,000, now seek informational interviews with their prospective physicians. Given the personal nature of the delivery of medical care, a face-to-face interview seems a reasonable approach to learning about one's physician. However, even though many consumers come armed with questions regarding evening and weekend coverage, telephone call-in policies, clinical training and experience, etc., numbers of them exit from these interviews uncertain of what they have learned. Moreover, they often still do not know how good a diagnostician the physician is, the compatibility of that consumer with the specialists to whom the physician would refer, or the answers on a number of highly relevant and important issues. It is not clear whether much of this information is measurable and could be provided to consumers, even if provider organizations wished to do so.

Selection of a health insurance or managed care plan is likely to be only a slightly more informed process. Instead of turning to a neighbor, as noted above, an employee might turn to the adjacent employee (who knows as much as the neighbor, limited only to his or her personal experiences) or to the health benefits officer at the place of employment. That benefits officer at least has the benefit of hearing a larger number of employees criticize or praise various health plans and packages, allowing the formation of a more knowledgeable opinion. In spite of the wealth of information that employers and health plans may provide at open enrollment periods, it appears that much of it is not used. As one study noted: "Families tend to rely primarily on information obtained by word of mouth from just a few individuals or on personal experience as a patient. These findings reinforce the notion that high involvement does not necessarily produce substantial systematic search behavior. Health care consumers appear to use simple heuristics when obtaining information about providers, relying on friends, family, or other health care professionals."[2]

Information regarding the choice of hospitals available through a health plan is generally considered to be useful because consumers believe that they have informed preferences for hospitals. Choice of hospitals is one of the major attributes influencing consumer choice of health plans.[3]

However, there is much information that consumers would find most useful but do not feel is available to them. In focus group research, consumers speak of wanting to know, for example, if they or their spouses get breast cancer, will the health plan be willing to pay for a bone marrow transplant (still viewed by some as an experimental treatment)? Will the plan pay for organ transplants if they are needed? Will the plan cover infertility treatments, and, if so, how many cycles and what type of treatment? This information is often not available to the consumer in advance of purchase because these are treatments for which the policy may vary by type of patient and by course of the disease. Lawsuits filed by managed care members against their managed care organizations seeking coverage of these treatments indicate an expectation of coverage by members who interpreted the policy different from the way the organization intended it to be interpreted. The existence of a policy for deciding coverage is often not sufficient to provide consumers with the perception that they know fully what is and is not covered.

Neither of these major health care purchase decisions—choosing a physician or a health plan/insurance package—could be portrayed as informed choice. However, as of mid-1994, a movement to provide more information to consumers has begun to manifest itself. Referred to by many as "report cards," measures of performance across a number of health related activities are starting to be publicly reported.

For example, managed care plans such as U.S. Healthcare, Inc., United HealthCare Corp., and Kaiser Permanente have begun to publicize to their members and to the business community their rates of childhood immunization, mammography screenings, prenatal checkups, and cholesterol testing. These performance measures (referred to as HEDIS or Health Plan Employer Data and Information Set), piloted by the National Committee for Quality Assurance (see chapter 5), are similar to the types of information being measured or proposed by the Joint Commission on Accreditation of Healthcare

Organizations, the RAND Corporation, and other interested parties. *How* these report cards will be used is not clear yet, in large part because of the uncertainty as to *what* will be measured; while HEDIS measures are specified for the present moment, they could be expected to change because of feedback from employers and consumers. Implicitly it is assumed that consumers should and will want to see these data. As we will see, there are reasons to question this assumption.

Desired versus Provided Data

Wise health care managers will recognize quickly that the mere provision of data does not guarantee their use or desirability. Automobile safety data, for instance, have been available for years and are published annually in newspapers across the country when the National Highway and Traffic Safety Council releases its yearly safety study results. Yet very few consumers attend to the data or purchase automobiles based solely on information the data provide; if they had, the market share of Volvos (routinely rated as one of the safest cars) would have been a lot higher, even if one considers only those who could afford to buy Volvos. Obviously, one reason for this is that some consumers may value styling, options, or other attributes of a car over safety.

Similarly, the publication or availability of mammography and childhood immunization rates does not necessarily mean that consumers will either want those data or use them. The HEDIS data and similar data were collected to inform the employer constituency; employers have a vested interest in seeing that these preventive and early disease detection measures are used, because, in the long run, they save not only lives but also money. To a large extent, this perspective, which focuses on aggregate costs and benefits, also matches closely with the public health perspective.

Consumers, however, rarely take an aggregated cost/benefit approach in selecting their health care providers or plans. Their approach is instead highly individualistic and personalized. A woman who is interested in mammography cares only if her health plan covers the cost and provides access to mammography for her. That the plan may not pay for mammography for *all* other women is irrelevant to her as long as she is covered. Therefore, the overall plan mammography rate, while it might be suggestive of the individual's likelihood of receiving a mammogram, is not likely to be highly desirable information from the woman's perspective. The same may be said for many of the other types of information currently being provided by the first iteration of "report cards." There is nothing to guarantee that the information is desirable, let alone compelling, from a consumer perspective.

Types of Information Desired by Consumers

Many studies have been done on what type of information consumers want to see in health care advertising,[4,5] because health care organizations that had never before undertaken advertising wanted to know how to spend their advertising dollars wisely. The information that consumers cited was far-ranging, but also respectful of the type of information that one could and could not expect to see (or hear) in an advertisement. For a physician, specialty, board eligibility or board certification, hours during which the physician was available, languages spoken, types of insurance and credit cards taken, availability of laboratory and x-ray services on the premises, and hospitals to which the physician admitted were all specified by consumers as being useful information.

More interesting was the type of information for which consumers expressed a great desire but which they never expected to see, because, to their knowledge (which was correct at the time and, to a large extent, still is), such information did not exist: personalized outcome data. They wanted to have information that could tell them: What is the likely outcome of this surgery for me? What is the probability that this medicine will cure me or relieve me of my symptoms? Outcomes research is still in its infancy, although funding for it is significant enough that we can expect a dramatic growth in outcomes databases.

It is very important to note, however, the limited usefulness of *outcomes information* unless it is *personalized* to the individual. As stated above, consumers tend not to use aggregated data nearly as well as personalized data. Data that state that a certain surgery gives *all* individuals receiving that particular surgery a 40 percent chance of getting significantly better and a 60 percent chance of getting worse is not helpful to most people. These numbers still do not tell them if, given their health histories, the skill of their surgeon, the quality of their postoperative care, and so on, they are likely to fall into the 40 percent or the 60 percent.

A format that most consumers would find more useful would be outcomes data personalized to their own health histories, demographics, and life-style preferences. Such a format is available (or will be shortly) from the Foundation for Informed Medical Decision Making (see Chapter 18.) Using interactive videodisc technology, this not-for-profit organization is creating programs, based on highly credible outcomes research, that will let the consumer sit down with user-friendly technology and, once having answered a variety of health history, life-style, and other questions, that will be able to tell the consumer the likeliest outcome that he or she faces as a result of a specific procedure or course of treatment.

Process versus Outcome

The public health perspective of cost/benefit has always viewed benefits in terms of outcomes (mortality statistics, for example.) Now, with the advent of methodologies to measure medical outcomes with far more refinement, we can anticipate an even greater focus on outcomes as the primary variables to be measured. However, from a consumer and managerial perspective, this is insufficient.

The recent literature[6-8] in the field of service marketing—and this literature is certainly relevant to health care—suggests that consumers are more likely to judge health care services by the *process* of delivery than by its *outcome*. It is not uncommon, for example, to hear someone say that his or her hospital stay was terrible and that he or she would never return to that hospital, even though the outcome of that hospital visit was highly positive. Similarly, a family member may rave about a physician who took care of an elderly mother, even though the elderly mother died (the ultimate in a negative outcome!). In both these cases, as is typical in health care, the process overwhelmed the outcome.

In the studies of desired advertising content, consumers stated a strong desire for process information but did not expect to see it because they believed that the data did not exist: how long one would have to wait to get an appointment with a physician for specific types of medical problems; how long patients could expect to wait in the physician's waiting room and, once undressed, in the physician's examination room; how respectful the physician and related service providers were of the patients; how much time the physician spent with the patient; and so on. It is process, rather than outcomes, that appears to be most strongly linked to consumer satisfaction.

This information can be gathered through *consumer research* (asking consumers how long they had to wait in the waiting room, how well their physicians listened to them, and so on). Xerox Corp., Digital Equipment, and GTE Corp. together, for example, have surveyed 35,000 of their employees regarding their satisfaction levels with their health plans (see Chapter 2). The survey includes information on the ease of seeing physicians, waiting times, and perceived quality of physician care. This information is to be distributed to the companies' employees, who can then use it to make more informed decisions based on the experiences of fellow employees. Measures of patient or consumer perceptions, preferences, and satisfaction are commonly used in other industries. These industries recognize that, even if consumer perceptions do not reflect fact (e.g., the patient thought he or she had waited an hour in the physician's waiting room, even though it was in fact only 45 minutes), they are the bases on which consumers make their decisions.

This information can also be collected through the systematic gathering of *operational data*. Health care organizations should routinely collect waiting time data, for example, not merely to provide it to consumers, but also to use to improve the operational performance of the organization. How long does the average caller to an HMO pediatrics service stay on hold? How many times do parents get fed up with waiting to get taken off hold and hang up, leaving the medical problems of their children unsolved? How often does an x-ray film have to be redone because of poor quality? Which phlebotomists routinely have to attempt more than once to draw blood? In health care settings, such measures are beginning to appear in organizations that are truly committed to total quality management

Another valuable source of management information is *consumer complaints*. Most complaints focus on process issues. They provide direction to management regarding sources of consumer dissatisfaction and give guidance as to where management ought to place its efforts and resources. Formal measurement and categorization of complaints can often substitute for more costly consumer research. While this may not be information that consumers want to see, complaints constitute information that managers should collect and measure. Further, managers should develop structured systems of response to consumer complaints; otherwise they risk greater dissatisfaction from a failure to respond.

A particular type of information, a mix of process and outcome, that is becoming increasingly more important to consumers is *access information*. Consumers are very concerned, and therefore want more information about, access: Will they be able to join the panel of the primary car physician whom they select, or will that physician be unwilling to take more patients from that particular managed care organization? Will their managed care plan try to bar access to the primary care physician, requiring the patient to see a nurse practitioner first? Will unreasonably long waiting times ostensibly deny them speedy access to medical care? Will they be able to see a specialist if they need to do so? How long will they have to wait if they need physical therapy? Any measures of access provided by health care organizations will be heartily welcomed by consumers.

Limits to Consumer Use of Information

It is rare for consumers to turn down offers of information. That does not mean, however, that they will use the information. The federal government, for instance, provides a phenomenal amount of publicly available data on products and services, ranging from the nutritional content of foods to the costs and benefits of various financial investment vehicles. Rarely are these data used in consumer purchase decisions.

There are two reasons for the lack of consumer use of data. First, some information may not be meaningful to consumers. HEDIS data, for example, presented in an aggregated fashion, may not have meaning to those who deal best with personalized information. Or information on childhood immunizations may not matter to families whose children are already grown. Second, what promises to be a far greater problem in the future, with the arrival of large numbers of health care report cards, is that consumers will be given too much information, too much to analyze:

"The assumption among some consumer advocates and government agencies is that consumers should be supplied with as much information as possible to permit a comparison of brand alternatives. The same assumption underlies economic theory: Optimal choice requires access to information on all alternatives. The reality, however, is that consumers rarely seek all of the available information. The cost of search and the complexity of processing are just too great to attempt to consider all brand alternatives. Therefore, more information is not necessarily better. In fact, too much information may create information overload, that is, confusion in the decision task resulting in an ineffective decision."[9]

The risk that the health care field faces, then, if consumers are unable to deal effectively with all the information provided to them, is that they will oversimplify the data. They may seek only a very few numbers to represent, however inadequately, the complexity of the total data set. Capon and Burke[10] found consumers used only 24 percent of available information in evaluating choices for a high-involvement (high-risk) purchases; an even lower finding, 2 percent of available data used, was found by Jacoby![11]

Another example of ineffective use of data in the health care field was provided in a popular consumer science magazine:

"Health statistics may be hazardous to our mental health. Inundated by numbers purporting to predict everything from our likelihood of dying from cancer to our chances of contracting AIDS, we respond with a curious range of reactions that rarely reflect the true nature of the alleged risk. We ignore real dangers while reacting emotionally to phantoms; we blithely accept dubious conclusions while disbelieving sensible ones; or we simply (or not so simply) misinterpret the numbers."[12]

In the health plan selection decision process, there is also the potential for misinterpretation of the numbers, especially as the available numbers become more plentiful because of the advent of health care organization report cards. If the data on health plan alternatives are too confusing for them, consumers may revert to their historical information sources—neighbors, fellow workers, etc.

This does not deny the need to produce data for consumers. It suggests that the health care field ought to be attuned to measuring performance issues that matter to consumers and then present that information in ways that are clear and understandable to them. This includes process as well as outcomes information. To the extent possible, it should be personalized; a consumer wants to know not the average waiting time in all plan physicians' offices, but the waiting time in the office of the one physician whom that patient routinely sees. And, finally, we need to recognize that, no matter how good a job we do of providing information to consumers, much of the information will not be used because consumers often fall upon heuristics to simplify their decision making. However, as consumers come to expect increasing amounts of health care information that is relevant and meaningful to them as individuals, we might hope for a greater ability and likelihood on their part to decide on the basis of this information.

References

1. Markello, R. and Vorhous, C. "Selecting a Pediatrician." Graduate student project for the Boston University Health Care Management Program, Dec. 1978.

2. Stewart, D., and others. "Information Search and Decision Making in the Selection of Family Health Care." *Journal of Health Care Marketing* 9(2):29-39, June 1989.

3. Chakratory, G., and others. "How Consumers Choose Health Insurance." *Journal of Health Care Marketing* 14(1):21-33, Spring 1994.

4. Miller, J., and Waller, R. "Health Care Advertising: Consumer vs. Physician Attitudes." *Journal of Advertising* 8(4):20-9, Fall 1979.

5. McAlexander, J., and others. "Positioning Health Care Services: Yellow Pages Advertising and Dental Practice Performance." *Journal of Health Care Marketing* 13(1):54-7, Winter 1993.

6. Zeithaml, V. "How Consumer Evaluation Processes Differ between Goods and Services." In *Marketing of Services*, Donnelly, J., and George, W., Eds. Chicago, Ill.: American Marketing Association, 1981, pp. 186-90.

7. Berry, L. "Big Ideas in Service Marketing." *Journal of Consumer Marketing* 3(2):47-51, Spring 1986.

8. Berry, L., and Parasuraman, A. *Marketing Services: Competing through Quality.* New York, N.Y.: The Free Press, 1991.

9. Assael, H. *Consumer Behavior and Marketing Action.* Boston, Mass.: PWS-Kent Publishing Co., 1992, p. 167.

10. Capon, N., and Burke, M. "Individual, Product Class, and Task-Related Factors in Consumer Information Processing." *Journal of Consumer Research* 7(3):314-26, Dec. 1980.

11. Jacoby, J. "Prepurchase Information Acquisition. In *Advances in Consumer Research*, Vol. 3, Anderson, B., Ed. Atlanta, Ga.: Association for Consumer Research, 1975, pp. 306-14.

12. Paulos, J. "Counting on Dyscalculia." *Discover* 15(3):30-5, March 1994.

CHAPTER 4

What Information Do Managers of Health Care Organizations Need to See: A Physician Manager's Perspective?

by Charles M. Cutler, MD, MS

"**A**s a monitor, the manager perpetually scans his or her environment for information, interrogates liaison contacts and subordinates, and receives unsolicited information, much of it as a result of the network of personal contacts he or she has developed. Remember that a good part of the information that a manager collects in the monitor role arrives in oral form, often as gossip, hearsay, and speculation. By virtue of contacts, the manager has a natural advantage in collecting this soft information for his or her organization."*

In the hierarchy of most health care organizations, the physician executive is responsible for the quality of care and service provided to patients, clients, or customers. It is the physician executive who interprets information with an understanding of clinical concerns, processes of care, and clinical operations. The physician executive therefore needs enough information to be sure that the care provided produces optimal patient outcomes and is delivered in the most cost-effective manner.

In the context of quality management (TQM, CQI, etc.), all measures are indicators of different aspects of processes or systems. This chapter addresses formal information systems and a provider framework with which to use this information. Nevertheless, the physician executive should keep in mind the importance of informal sources as well.

Volume, Outcome, Process, and Structure

We can classify measures of care into four categories: volume, outcome, process, and structure.

---

* Mintzberg, H. *Mintzberg on Management.* New York, N.Y.: The Free Press, 1989.

Volume measures assess the input that enters the care process. The number of members in an HMO, admissions per month to the hospital, fluid intake, or number of requests for a procedure are all volumes of input.

Outcome measures are the results of the process: five-year survival rates, health plan member retention rates, physician turnover rates, etc. These measures are the results of processes that take a relatively long time, so they are performed regularly but not frequently. We can also use intermediate measures of outcome, such as the rate of patients responding to therapy, member satisfaction rates, and staff satisfaction rates. While it may be appropriate to obtain these measures more frequently to provide an "early" warning, the time it takes to generate even these intermediate measures (cycle time) is relatively long. In order to know how we are doing in a more timely manner, and in order to know how to improve performance that is below standard, we need to understand the process involved and identify key process measures.

Process measures are important indicators of how well a process is working (process control) and are intermediate indicators of outcomes. Process measures should be chosen at key points in the process—that is, those that are subject to variation and those that are critical to reaching the best outcome. The ability to identify these measures requires a good understanding of the process and of important control points. The precise measures we choose to monitor will change over time as we understand the process better (table 1, below).

Structural measures are those that describe "fixed" aspects of a system: the distance to the hospital for a given population, the capacity of laboratory equipment, or the capacity to provide patient care (e.g., number of pediatricians). These measures are important in planning and understanding changes in outcome or process measures: If patients are too far from the mammography center (structure), the percentage of women who have mammograms (process) will be low, the incidence of breast cancer

TABLE 1. TYPICAL PROCESS MEASURES

User	Measure	Process	Outcome
Group Practice Department Chief	Waiting time for appointments	Access to care	Member retention
Chief of Surgery	CABG pump time	CABG	Patient survival
HMO Medical Director	Hospital days per 1,000 members	Hospital care of patients	Cost of hospital care
Hospital Medical Director	Average cost/patient by DRG	Hospital care	Profitability
Chief of Pediatrics	Immunization rate	Preventive care	Prevention of infection

TABLE 2. EXAMPLES OF MEASURES			
Dimension	Outcome	Process	Structure
Cost	Cost of successful CABG	Cost of OR time	Cost of hospital plant
Service	Member satisfaction and retention	Time on "hold"	Travel time to MD
	Surgeon satisfaction and retention	Waiting time for OR	Number of ORs available
Quality	Pediatric immunization rate	Preventive care	Distance to office
	Asthmatic without dyspnea	Use of inhaled steriods	Baseline pulmonary function

beyond stage I will be higher (intermediate outcome), and the mortality of these patients will be higher (outcome).

Dimensions of Measurement: Cost, Service and Quality

Organizations can measure their performance in many different dimensions, but the ones we use most commonly in health care are cost, service, and clinical quality (table 2, above).

In the past, many organizations did not develop the systems necessary to track costs in a detailed manner. Efficient management of the cost of care is now crucial to an organization's success. The physician manager brings the clinical perspective with which to analyze costs of care but is dependent on others in the organization to track and display costs in enough detail to be able to take action on specific processes or steps in a process.

Service is the perceived value the user receives. Service may reflect the character of the interaction between patient and provider, the access the surgeon receives to the operating room, or the speed with which the office answers the phone.

Quality is conformance to specifications or standards. Clinical quality is the assessment of care against the best possible clinical outcome (gold standard). Is the network of physicians board-certified? Is the mortality associated with the procedure less than the national average? Is the childhood immunization rate up to standard?

Deciding What to Measure

The first major challenge for physician executives is identifying the outcomes that most determine the success of the organization. Are they measures of volume, outcome, process, or structure? Are they cost, service, or quality? For most organizations, it will be a combination of all of these measures. Most health care consumers and purchasers (employers, patients, and insurers) want the most "value." Value is generally perceived as the highest quality for the lowest cost.

$$V = Q/P \text{ (value equals quality divided by price)}$$

Dashboard Measures

The physician executive needs measures that monitor the performance of the organization in a continuous, aggregate manner. These measures should be easy to obtain and should be indicative of the performance of the organization as whole. They should be few enough to display regularly and diverse enough so that they provide a warning if there are problems with any part of the system. They are called "dashboard measures" because they indicate performance in the same way that the dashboard of the car provides measures of the car's and driver's performance. As with the car's dashboard, they may include warning lights that notify the physician executive to investigate the problem more intensely, i.e., collect more detailed information (table 3, below).

Most of these measures are straightforward or can be easily determined through standard accounting techniques for cost measures. Quality and service measures are more difficult to identify and measure. They fall into service (perceived quality) measures determined through market research and outcomes measures, such as low-birthweight infants.

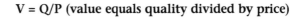

TABLE 3. DASHBOARD MEASURES	
Customer	**Measure**
Managed Care Medical Director	Admissions per 1,000
	Referrals per 1,000
	Readmission rate
	Physician turnover
Hospital Executive	Average cost/admission
	Waiting time for elective surgery or utilization/capacity of OR
	Nosocomial infection rate
Corporate Medical Director	Employee sick days per month
	Number of work-related injuries reported
Department Chief	Number of visits per week
	Waiting time of appointments
	Number of readmissions

Cost

Dashboard measures for cost are the easiest to obtain, because all organizations have the level of financial data necessary for billing clients, reporting to the board of directors, and providing information to regulators (table 4, below).

In an HMO, revenue is directly related to the number of members. In most cases, the average premium revenue per member will not change greatly from month to month unless there is a major influx from a new group whose premium is significantly different from the rest of the membership's. Per member costs, on the other hand, exhibit much more variation. They are tied to utilization for the membership, which varies significantly each month and season. The HMO physician executive therefore focuses intently on managing average cost per member.

TABLE 4. COST DASHBOARD MEASURES

User	Measure
HMO Medical Director	Cost per member per month
	Admission per 1,000 per month (or total admissions)
	Hospital days per 1,000 members per month
	Referral costs per month
Hospital Medical Director	Cost of selected DRGs
	Hospital census

In a traditional fee-for-service group, average revenue exhibits more variation than does the cost of operating the practice. The cost measures for the physician executive in a fee-for-service group practice may be the billings per month, the average charge per patient, the number of patients seen, or the number of procedures per month.

Of course, cost cannot be considered in the absence of an understanding of the strategic goals of the organization, the product lines, the components that make up the cost structure, or the costs that competitors incur. It may be useful to think of cost in classic accounting terms: fixed and variable, operating and capital, short- and long-term. It is also useful to think of costs as they relate to steps in the process. For physician executives, this information is frequently aggregated into categories such as outpatient care, inpatient care, pharmacy, ancillary services, etc. This allows the physician executive to understand the relative importance and contribution of these areas to total costs. This information is not useful unless there is a benchmark. Many industry groups collect benchmarks through surveys: Group Health Association of America or Marion-Merrell-Dow for HMOs, American Hospital Association for hospitals, Medical Group Management Association for group practices, etc.

Even in the absence of benchmarks, the physician executive uses cost information to target those areas that are most likely to produce savings. In order to do so, more information about the components of cost is necessary. This includes measures of utilization that generates costs (admissions, length of stay, visits, procedures, etc.) as well as the cost per unit. Depending on the structure of the organization, these volume indicators may need to be normalized for a population or trended over time to be useful. For example, any organization working under a capitation payment will need to normalize the volume per unit of population for it to be useful. For organizations paid on a fee-for-service basis, the cost is normalized per visit.

"Dashboard" data are useful in raising questions about the cost of specific processes or process steps that may need further investigation and in ad hoc data collection. For example, an HMO notes a rise in outpatient costs per member. Further investigation of routine data may identify an increase in radiology costs. It requires considerable additional analysis to identify MRI costs as the main contributor and even more investigation to identify the use of MRI for evaluation of patients with knee pain as the dominant factor.

The focus of analysis of costs has shifted in recent years from the cost per unit, such as cost per visit or procedure, to cost per diagnosis. This has been stimulated by DRGs and managed care. Most practices and hospitals now depend on finding the most cost-effective manner to manage a patient's illness. The good news is that this allows us to evaluate patient care in the most comprehensive manner; the bad news is that data sources most physician managers currently have available cannot be aggregated easily or comprehensively to understand the cost of a given illness.

Consider a simple example—the cost of prenatal care and delivery of a normal healthy child in a staff-model HMO. Information about the prenatal care may be difficult to obtain unless the HMO has a system that tracks fees for services or some equivalent. Many staff-model HMOs do not collect this information. Even if they track number of visits by the member and the use of some specific services, such as radiology or laboratory, it will probably be difficult to aggregate the data into an estimate of the costs of the visits themselves. In addition, the more services are paid under a capitation contract, the more likely it is that detailed information about those costs will not be available. The need for more complete information should be made clear prior to contracting with providers, because the providers will need to supply it to the plan, even if they are not paid on a fee-for-service basis.

The physician executive needs enough information on a regular and timely basis to monitor the key cost drivers, the organization's relation to the competition, and its trends over time and must be able to dig further into the components of costs to be able to manage them.

Service
Service information is frequently not routinely available without a system set up specifically to support it. The first step is to identify key measures of service that can serve as dashboard measures (table 5, page 33). These are generally identified through customer surveys (see Chapter 11).

Service measures should be linked to key attributes of customer satisfaction. For example, quick telephone access may be very important to the customer. Time on hold can be correlated with satisfaction or dissatisfaction (such as consumer complaints). The

TABLE 5. SERVICE DASHBOARD MEASURES		
User	**Outcome Measure**	**Process Measure**
HMO Medical Director	Member satisfaction rate	Waiting time for appointments Time on hold "How was your visit" survey results
Hospital Medical Director	Physician satisfaction	Access to OR Turnaround time on lab reports
Industrial Medical Director	Employee satisfaction	Sign-up rate for worksite education program

organization can then measure time on hold or percentage of calls put on hold to know if it is in the range that satisfies members. If the physician executive waits for a satisfaction survey or for member complaints to rise, damage has already been done.

Similarly, consider access to the operating room (OR). If the manager knows that surgeons can tolerate a one-week wait for other than urgent cases, it is possible just to monitor the waiting time and, if it is rising, make changes before surgeons take their cases to another hospital.

On the other hand, many service measures (for example, attendance at orientation sessions) are not linked to customer satisfaction and are not useful. They may even cloud the picture by diverting attention to measures that customers do not care about. Managers can identify what information is important by a sophisticated analysis of customer satisfaction surveys. A regression or correlation analysis of individual results and overall satisfaction can provide these data.

Quality
Data about the technical quality of care are most difficult to obtain and evaluate. There are many challenges for the medical manager: what measures or standards are important; what data are necessary to evaluate performance against these standards; and how can the data be obtained in an efficient, effective, and accurate manner?

Quality Measures and Standards
It can be very difficult to develop quality standards that clinicians will agree on beyond very gross measures such as mortality rates, immunization rates, pap smear screening rates, etc. Even with common conditions, it can be difficult to reach agreed measures of performance. For example, it is easy for clinicians to agree that patients with hypertension should have their blood pressure controlled all of the time, but there is less agreement on the level of blood pressure that represents good control or the percentage of patients whose blood pressure should be under 140/90 after a year of treatment.

Some outcomes measures are the result of complex processes. While clinicians may agree the outcome is important and may even agree to a goal, they may perceive the most important contributions to the outcomes to be outside their control (e.g., low-birthweight infants) and therefore not remediable.

Data Collection

Still, there are measures that are important and that clinicians can agree on. The challenge becomes the measurement. Where are the data available? The best source for data is one that can be electronically retrieved and analyzed. There are only a few sources of these data: claims or billing data; clinical services that routinely track their data in computer databases, such as pharmacy, lab or radiology; and those practices that are fortunate enough to have computerized medical records.

Claims data, while useful, are limited in a number of ways. Claims may not capture or may inconsistently capture the necessary data. Claims capture demographic data, date of service, diagnosis (sometimes only one and not all diagnoses), and procedures. For some analyses, claims-based reports are fine as a first step or as a monitor. Because procedures frequently generate claims or billing records, many practices know how many of their patients have had a procedure such as a mammogram. A claim can provide the age of the patient and date of the procedure. It does not usually provide an accurate reason for the procedure or the result. If the frequency of the procedure is high, additional data will be needed to understand why the rate is high, and those data are not likely to be available from claims. For example, hysterectomy rates can easily be calculated from claims data, but to understand the reasons for these rates, additional clinical information will be necessary. These data will usually require a much more labor-intensive process, such as chart review.

Summary

A framework that allows the physician executive to monitor volume, process, outcome and structure for quality, cost, and service will allow him or her to manage the important processes of care and service for the organization. Although data sources are far from perfect in most health care organizations, important data sources do exist, can be used, and can be improved.

It is as important for the physician executive to use "clinical judgment" in the collection and analysis of information as in patient management. Some of the criteria used to chose measures are management science, but many are informal. It is important to maintain informal information sources, because they provide insight into potential problems or explanations for variances from expected results. Brief conversations with clinicians can uncover a flu epidemic leading to increased admissions, changes in the OR scheduling leading to longer waiting times, or loss of a receptionist leading to longer times on hold. These informal sources can provide early warnings as well as clearer solutions to problems.

CHAPTER 5

Information Requirements:
Managers of Health Care Organizations

by Janet M. Corrigan, PhD, MBA

A physician executive of a managed care organization confronts significant challenges during these turbulent times of health reform and health system restructuring. Reliable information on health plan and provider performance is essential to focus limited resources and talents on areas of strategic importance in responding to the needs of an enrolled population and in securing the long-term future of the organization.

Senior management must perform multiple roles. First, it must ensure that the health care organization is responsive to the demands of its "customers," be they individuals or private and public purchaser representatives. Second, it must provide the leadership necessary to promote improvements in the accessibility and the quality of clinical care available to the organization's enrolled population. Third, because most health care organizations represent only one component of a community's health system, effective management also involves collaboration with other community leadership to address public health priorities. Fulfilling these multiple roles requires access to various types of information on clinical care provided by one's own organization and by other health care organizations.

In recent years, large employers have been particularly persistent and persuasive in demanding information from health care plans to assess quality of, accessibility to, and satisfaction with care as well as the cost of care. Some progress has been made toward the establishment of a "common set of performance measures" that health plans might provide to all purchasers, thus simplifying the data collection and reporting processes. This standard set of measures is known as the Health Plan Employer Data and Information Set (HEDIS).[1]

HEDIS

The first version of HEDIS, released in September 1991, was developed by The HMO Group (an association of group- and staff-model health plans), Kaiser Permanente, four large employers (Bull HN Information Systems, Digital Equipment Corporation, GTE Corporation, and Xerox Corporation), and Towers Perrin. In October 1992, the National Committee for Quality Assurance, an accreditation organization for the managed care industry, assembled a committee of employers and health plan representatives to further enhance the set of performance measures. This resulted in the release of Version 2.0 in November 1993[1,2] and an updated version, 2.5, in January 1995.

HEDIS 2.0/2.5 include more than 60 performance measures falling into four major areas—quality, access and patient satisfaction, membership and utilization, and finance (see table below). HEDIS 2.0/2.5 also encourages plans to provide purchasers with descriptive information on health plan management and activities that are not specifically quantifiable, such as provider credentialing and quality improvement program activities.

SUMMARY OF HEDIS 2.0/2.5 PERFORMANCE MEASURES

Quality of Care	Access & Satisfaction	Membership & Utilization	Finance
Preventive Medicine ∎ Childhood Immunization ∎ Cholesterol Screening ∎ Mammography Screening ∎ Cervical Cancer Screening **Prenatal Care** ∎ Low Birthweight ∎ Prenatal Care in the First Trimester **Acute and Chronic Disease** ∎ Asthma Inpatient Admission Rate ∎ Diabetic Retinal Exam **Mental Health** ∎ Ambulatory Follow-up after Hospitalization for Major Affective Disorders	**Access** ∎ Members with Plan Visit in Previous Three Years ∎ Number and Percent of Primary Care Physicians Accepting New Patients ∎ Plan Access Standards for Visits and Telephone Response **Member Satisfaction** ∎ Percent of Members "Satisfied" with the Plan ∎ Plan Satisfaction Surveys	∎ Enrollment/Disenrollment ∎ High Occurrence/High Cost Diagnoses and Procedures ∎ Inpatient Utilization ∎ Ambulatory Care Utilization ∎ Utilization (Nonacute Care) ∎ Maternity Care ∎ Newborn Care ∎ Mental Health Treatment ∎ Chemical Dependency Treatment ∎ Outpatient Drug Utilization	∎ Liquidity ∎ Efficiency ∎ Compliance with Statutory Requirements ∎ Premium Trends

HEDIS 2.0/2.5 measures represent only a core set of indicators—they do not constitute a comprehensive performance measurement system. There are only nine quality of care measures in HEDIS 2.0/2.5, and only three of them address chronic conditions. Not all measures lend themselves to straightforward interpretation (e.g., there are numerous factors in addition to access to appropriate prenatal care that affect a health plan's rate of low-birthweight babies).

Shaping and Responding to Information Needs
Physician managers play a pivotal role in shaping and responding to the information needs of their health care organization's customers. The HEDIS 2.0/2.5 data were provided by many health care organizations to their external customers for the first time in

1994 and 1995. This will likely give rise to more and more questions regarding performance. Therefore, physician managers will need to identify any factors that might explain why their organization's performance in a particular area is less than expected or less than that of other health plans. For example, a high disenrollment rate might be attributable to dissatisfaction stemming from inadequate access to providers, or it might possibly be the result of business foreclosures, layoffs, or relocations. To effectively respond, physician managers need access to increasingly sophisticated clinical information systems that are well integrated with administrative datasets that contain information on enrollee demographics and utilization patterns.

A health care organization's performance on HEDIS 2.0/2.5 measures will likely affect its competitive position in the community, so that physician managers will face increasing pressure to demonstrate improvement. A successful short-term strategy might be to target quality measurement and improvement efforts in the selected clinical areas addressed in HEDIS 2.0/2.5 (e.g., increasing cervical cancer screening rates), but this will not serve an organization well over the long run, because, as HEDIS evolves and undergoes periodic revision, it will likely represent a "moving target." Work is now starting on an enhanced set of measures, HEDIS 3.0. Over the long run, the most successful health plans will be those that build effective systems to improve performance in many areas.

Leadership in Clinical Care Improvement

This brings us to the second role of senior management—to provide the leadership necessary to promote improvements in the accessibility, quality, and appropriateness of clinical care available to the organization's enrolled population. To carry out this responsibility, physician managers need information on various aspects of performance, including:

- **Measures of Access and Service.** This refers to timeliness and appropriate level of service, as well as identification of underutilization and overutilization.

- **Measures of Clinical Care.** This encompasses both assessment of performance against established practice guidelines and the evaluation of clinical outcomes.

- **Measures of Enrollee Satisfaction and Health**. Enrollees are the ultimate judges of the acceptability of a health plan, including adequacy of the benefits provided, access to and organization of services, and satisfaction with interpersonal and technical aspects of care provided by primary care providers and specialists. Enrollees are also an excellent source of information on various aspects of health status, such as physical and social functioning, mental status, chronic conditions, and health risk behaviors (e.g., smoking).

- **Measures of Provider Satisfaction.** A health plan's primary care providers are in an excellent position to identify areas for improvement. In many instances, their input may represent an early warning signal of potential system problems that may have a deleterious impact on patient care. Physicians also play such an integral role in a health plan that maintaining high levels of satisfaction for them is essential to the long-term success of the health plan.

It is also important to capture and analyze trends in various types of operational data that may provide an indication of areas for improvement. Examples include enrollee complaints and grievances, disenrollment rates, coverage denials, and provider terminations.

Although it is possible to generate a long list of information requirements, it is more useful to identify key characteristics of automated information systems required to support clinical management.

- **Core Datasets.** Certain "core" datasets are essential to produce reports on performance (e.g., HEDIS reports) and to identify samples of enrollees for detailed analysis (e.g., to conduct a medical record audit concerning diabetes). These include enrollment files (including demographic information), hospital discharge data, and ambulatory encounter data. Many health plans currently lack data pertaining to ambulatory encounters or lack complete, reliable, and accurately coded information on diagnoses.

- **Supplementary Datasets.** For the most part, core datasets contain information on enrollee demographics, diagnoses, and use of services. These data are useful for deriving many medical care process measures, such as proportion of diabetics having an annual eye exam. To derive additional medical care process and outcome measures, it is necessary to abstract medical records or to have access to other supplementary datasets. For example, laboratory data would be useful to obtain mean hemoglobin level for diabetics.

- **Linkage and Integration of Datasets.** Unique patient identifiers are necessary to examine complete patterns of treatment across various sites and levels of care and over time. Unique provider identifiers are necessary to construct provider profiles. It is also essential to have access to the technical resources necessary to produce reports based on data derived from multiple core/supplementary datasets.

- **Calculation of Performance Measures for Various Units of Analysis.** For external reporting and monitoring purposes, performance measures are generally calculated for a health plan as a whole or for a selected group of enrollees (e.g., commercial group enrollees). To understand better and act upon this information, it is helpful to be able to "roll down" or disaggregate to the level of provider groups or sites of care.

- **Access to Common Classification Systems.** Meaningful analysis of data necessitates grouping patients by clinical characteristics and/or services provided. Common classification systems used for this purpose include ICD-9-CM, DRGs, and CPT-4.[3-5] Furthermore, classifying patient encounters/discharges according to several grouping systems will facilitate making comparisons with other health plans or public health data sources (e.g., HEDIS 2.0/2.5 includes several measures that are calculated for individuals assigned to particular DRGs).

- **Flexible Information Systems.** Perhaps the most important characteristic of a health plan's information systems is that they be flexible and capable of responding to demands for data that are constantly in flux.

It is imperative that physician managers become more knowledgeable of their health plans' information infrastructures, not only their capabilities but also their limitations. Physician managers should play an active role in shaping the evolution of their plans' information support systems.

Leadership in Community Health

The third role of senior management is to provide leadership for, and participate in, communitywide efforts to address public health priorities. Health plans, along with hospitals, academic medical centers, group practices, and others, bear a responsibility to support communitywide efforts that will enhance the health of all residents. The leadership for such efforts may come from the state or local government, the private sector, or some combination.

Certain health care issues may be best addressed through cooperative community efforts. For example, public education programs to prevent violence, which accounts for an estimated $34 billion in health insurance and disability payments and another $145 billion in lost quality of life,[6,7] would be beneficial for both a health plan's enrollees and other residents in the community. In the face of increasingly restricted public funds to support such initiatives, health care institutions in a community will need to provide support for such efforts.

The Healthy People 2000 initiative of the U.S. Public Health Service has identified priority areas and has established goals for the nation.[8] Community-based monitoring and improvement efforts are now needed to achieve these goals. In order to establish and to gauge progress toward meeting community health priorities, certain protocols for data collection and performance measurement must be established. Health plans and other participants in the community health system will need to commit to the collection and sharing of the necessary data.

As more and more states embark on major health reform initiatives, it will be important to establish a proper balance between cooperative communitywide efforts that benefit all residents and competition between health care plans. Numerous states or communities are establishing community information systems as a mechanism to both introduce greater efficiencies into the health system and support community monitoring and reporting.[9]

In theory, the information needs to fulfill these various roles should be complementary; in practice, they may conflict or undermine each other. For example, childhood immunization rates are an area of interest to a health plan's customers, to a health plan for internal management purposes, and to the community-at-large. HEDIS 2.0/2.5 includes a childhood immunization performance measure for two-year-old children continuously enrolled in the health plan since birth or shortly thereafter. Limiting the measure to continuously enrolled children ensures that the health plan is held accountable only for those children for whom it had ample opportunity to provide care. For public health reporting purposes, the Centers for Disease Control has promulgated guidelines for assessing vaccination levels in clinic settings that define the target population as either children 24 to 35 months of age who have a record of at least one vaccination on file in the clinic or children 24 to 35 months of age who have ever been seen at the clinic.[10] A health plan that links financial incentives for individual physicians or group practices for internal management purposes may want to calculate immunization rates by group or individual provider and adjust for patient characteristics associated with less likelihood of seeking preventive services. Alternative approaches to measuring performance in a given area can result in confusion.

The trend toward standardization of data collection protocols and performance measures will place certain limitations on the development of internal quality measurement and improvement systems. For health plans with extensive automated data systems, calculation of alternative immunization rates may not be difficult. But for most health plans, data acquisition is fairly resource intensive and frequently involves abstraction of medical records or the use of special data collection instruments. Because most plans have limited resources to allocate to quality measurement and improvement, external demands for performance measurement data must be balanced against internal health plan demands.

Conclusion

In summary, the medical management of a health plan must perform multiple roles in the area of quality reporting, measurement, and improvement and must respond to the needs of various constituencies. As the demand for data and information on quality, access, and satisfaction increases, medical leadership must play an active role in shaping the information needs of various constituencies, both external and internal to the health plan. Medical leadership must also play a role in building the information infrastructure of the health plan to ensure that the health plan responds to the needs of its enrollees as well as those of the community-at-large.

References

1. *Health Plan Employer Data and Information Set, Version 2.0.* Washington, D.C.: National Committee For Quality Assurance, Nov. 1993.

2. Corrigan, J., and Nielsen, D. "Toward the Development of Uniform Reporting Standards for Managed Care Organizations: The Health Plan Employer Data and Information Set." *Joint Commission Journal on Quality Improvement* 19(12):566-75, Dec. 1993.

3. *International Classification of Diseases, 9th Revision, Clinical Modification.* Ann Arbor, Mich.: Commission on Professional and Hospital Activities, 1993.

4. *Diagnosis Related Groups, Version 10.0: Definitions Manual.* Wallingford, Conn.: 3M Health Information System, 1992.

5. *CPT 1993 Physicians' Current Procedural Terminology.* Chicago, Ill.: American Medical Association, 1992.

6. Mercy, J., and others. "Public Health Policy for Preventing Violence." *Health Affairs* 12(4):7-29, Winter 1993.

7. Miller, T., and others. "Victim Costs of Violent Crime and Resulting Injuries." *Health Affairs* 12(4):186-97, Winter 1993.

8. Public Health Service. *Healthy People 2000: National Health Promotion and Disease Prevention Objectives.* Washington, D.C.: Government Printing Office. DHHS 91-50213, 1990.

9. *Annual Report.* New York, N.Y.: John A. Hartford Foundation, 1993.

10. *Guidelines for Assessing Vaccination Levels of the 2-year-old Population in a Clinic Setting.* Atlanta, Ga.: Centers for Disease Control, Oct. 1992.

CHAPTER 6

Perspectives of a Hospital Physician Executive: What Information Do Hospital Managers Need to See?

by William F. Minogue, MD, FACP

The role of the hospital physician executive has evolved steadily over the past 25 years. With the advent of health care market reform, this process is certain to accelerate well into the next century. In order to provide the leadership necessary for hospitals to thrive in the future, physician executives must be armed with high-quality information. Whereas the traditional medical director concentrated mainly on quality and utilization data, in the future, in order to make a difference, he or she must have knowledge and skills in the use of information related to the entire integrated health care system and to the health and economic status of the communities served.

History: 1960-1980
Prior to the 1960s, very few hospitals had employed physicians in executive roles. As hospital care became more complex, forward-thinking hospitals began to engage such physicians at least on a part-time basis. Medical leadership in most hospitals was provided by elected chiefs of medical staffs, who usually served a maximum of two years, most of which was spent learning the job. Their role was, and still is, full of conflicts, because they must act as agents of hospitals and their patients, as well as representatives of medical staff bodies politic.

As hospital and medical staff governance became increasingly complex, many conscientious elected presidents of hospital medical staffs found the task overwhelming. It became necessary to provide information to the elected leaders to enable them to carry out their duties under the by-laws and as required by external accrediting bodies.

Quality assurance was focused almost entirely on structure and process and centered around "medical audit," wherein common diseases or procedures were studied intensively through chart review. Quality assurance programs were built on the premise that criteria-based chart review would make it obvious where medical staff members (individually and collectively) had learning gaps. Continuing medical education programs were to be the remedy. By the late 1970s, the Joint Commission on Hospitals, now the

Joint Commission on Accreditation of Healthcare Organizations, required a certain number of audits per discipline per year. The net effect was probably not worth the effort. It did, however, legitimize peer review as a concept and set the stage for more enlightened data collection.

With the *Darling* case,[1] where hospitals were held accountable for what took place within their walls, and the *Nork* case,[2] where medical staffs were deemed responsible for the quality of care provided by independent practitioners, the need for better and more focused information increased dramatically.

In 1965, with the passage of Medicare legislation, the Joint Commission overnight went from a consultative body to an inspector. Hospitals accredited by the Joint Commission were deemed reimbursable by Medicare. Joint Commission standards became more and more regulatory, and state licensing bodies followed suit. The need for medical managers to obtain information was once again magnified.

As we began to stratify data by specialty and by physician, physicians claimed their patients were sicker and the data were not valid. Comparative data, physician-to-physician and peer hospital-to-peer hospital, were sparse and not case mix-adjusted.

History: 1980-1990

Medicare Utilization and Quality Review

When Professional Standards Review Organizations (PSRO) and their successor the Professional Review Organizations (PROs) were formed to monitor utilization under Medicare, utilization review committees in hospitals found it essential to have diagnoses, procedures, and physician-specific information in order to effectively discharge their responsibilities. Later in the decade, PROs began to engage in quality review. This was a primitive and highly bureaucratic program and was largely redundant, as most hospitals were involved in far more extensive quality assessment than the PROs were.

Diagnosis-Related Groups (DRGs)

In 1981, DRGs were introduced in New Jersey. Information systems vendors and hospitals developed software programs marrying charge data and clinical information. This was essential if hospitals were to engage physicians in their efforts to maximize reimbursement. Some DRGs were profitable and others were not. It became valuable to stratify data by hospital length of stay, by use of laboratory and radiology services, by use of supplies and equipment, and by such measures as time in the operating room in order to get to the root causes of resource utilization. For the first time, physicians were asked to be good stewards by assisting hospitals in improvement of their financial performance. Considerable variation in physician practice patterns was observed, and, although this caused some early consternation among members of hospital staffs, such economic review has now become commonplace.

Outcomes Data and Research

In 1985, the Joint Commission, with its Agenda for Change, began its quest for measures of the outcomes of care. Since Avedis Donabedian[3] (in the '60s) wrote that quality consisted of structure, process, and outcome, we had spent nearly 20 years focusing

Measuring Clinical Care: A Guide for Physician Executives

almost entirely on structure and process because outcome measures were, and to a large extent remain, illusive. The Joint Commission, with its indicators project, is addressing outcomes measurement (see following chapter), and it has encountered frustrations and delays due to the difficulty of developing nationally applicable and reproducible data systems.

The Joint Commission has found that consensus and scientific validity are not easily attainable at a national level. Data collection in support of its program has frustrated beta test sites. Data systems in hospitals do not readily support such efforts. The cost of manual information gathering and the questionable impact once the data are assembled are frequently listed concerns.

The federal government created the Agency for Health Care Policy and Research (AHCPR) with the search for robust guidelines and outcomes measures as its principal mandate (see Chapter 17). This program is moving slowly and its full impact remains far in the future.

The California Medical Society, under the leadership of Joyce Craddick, MD,[4] introduced us to now commonly used outcomes indicators, and the Maryland Hospital Association (MHA) indicators project is a further manifestation of that approach. About 450 hospitals share data and benchmark on one another through the MHA program. Nosocomial infections, mortality, unplanned readmissions, and returns to special care units are some of the important indicators. The ambulatory patient monitors include unplanned returns to the emergency department (ED), patients in the ED longer than six hours, and patients who leave prior to treatment. Many hospitals have found these indicators valuable, as they are severity-adjusted and provide peer hospital comparisons. Their greatest utility is that they identify opportunities to address systems and process flows and invite users to continuously improve performance in the areas addressed. This provides medical leaders with peer hospital comparative data and has allowed medical staffs and hospital boards to better exercise their fiduciary responsibilities using external validators of care. These data have become major motivators for change when a hospital is significantly at variance with its peer group.

Practice Patterns

Professor John Wennberg at Dartmouth, with his small-area variation studies,[5] pointed out the striking differences in physician practice and utilization patterns largely attributable to training and habits developed during their formative years. These data have stimulated medical managers to look at the variability of physician resource utilization from a behavior modification rather than a "bad apples" perspective. Once physicians are exposed to peer comparison data, they commonly alter their practice patterns if they are significant outliers. The remaining variation is largely attributable to flows in the systems and processes the patients (and physicians) encounter in the course of care.

History: 1990-2000

Continuous Quality Improvement

By the beginning of the '90s, continuous quality improvement in health care was beginning to take root. Based on the successes of Deming, Juran, Crosby, and others in business and industry, medical managers were able to embrace a philosophy that was both scientifically based, through its emphasis on statistical quality control, and behaviorally sound. The philosophy is built on the finding that most variation results from poor systems and process design. For the first time in health care, we have an opportunity to manage by fact rather than anecdote. All processes generate data, and the medical manager must be a central figure in the development and analysis of these data. In order to maximally benefit from this new philosophy, it became necessary to collect data on the systems and processes of care and to monitor those processes forever.

Another characteristic of the quality movement is its passion for pleasing, and even delighting, the customer. It has become necessary to collect data regarding patient, physician, and employee satisfaction; community satisfaction; and even satisfaction of both the payers of heath care dollars and the vendors who provide us with goods and services.

The profound knowledge about processes generated through the use of cross-functional and department-specific quality improvement teams, with their run charts, control charts, scatter diagrams, Pareto charts, cause and effect diagrams, flow charts, and other quality tools, have introduced the physician executive to an entirely new world of information. Strategic quality planning, done correctly, creates another data requirement if the plans are to be deployed effectively. Physician executives are central here as well.

Clinical Guidelines and Clinical Pathways

Most specialty societies have developed clinical guidelines for common diseases and procedures, and they are being used by medical managers and medical staff leaders as benchmarks for clinical practice in hospitals. A marriage of outcomes data, clinical guidelines, and process improvement has resulted in the development of clinical (or critical) pathways of care. Instead of being looked at vertically as what physicians, nurses, the laboratory, the radiology department, social workers, administration, discharge planning, etc. do, an episode of care is viewed horizontally from the time the patient presents in a clinic or physician's office or emergency department until he or she has reached a steady state of recovery some weeks or months downstream. The construction and monitoring of these pathways is based on Deming's 94/6 rule (94 percent of variation is caused by the system and only 6 percent by individual performance). Bad outcomes in medicine are usually attributable to poor systems and process design (or no system at all). The use of paper and oral means of transmitting high-volume, critical patient care information invites error, waste, and rework at the myriad handoffs from provider to provider, shift to shift, discipline to discipline, and facility to facility. As "captains of the (clinical) ship," physicians have assumed most of the responsibility for bad outcomes. Good clinical pathways supported by clear and easily available data are beginning to standardize patient care to a level not possible using traditional quality assurance approaches. An enormous amount of data and information flows from these pathways, thus providing the physician executive with another addition to his or her data and information armamentarium.

By building in outcomes measures at the end of clinical pathways, individual physician executives in hospitals may be able to produce better clinical outcomes data than many of the research efforts to date. Through the use of assessments, including health status measurements such as the SF-36 Form, at the beginning and end of each pathway, individual managers will finally have powerful information about what works and does not work in medicine.

Juran speaks of quality planning, quality improvement, and quality control as the trilogy necessary to achieve world-class performance. The emphasis historically has been on quality control, and that must continue through the review of morbidity and mortality data as usual. Regulatory bodies, such as the states and the Joint Commission, will continue to require information in order to carry out their statutory or societal mandates for external review of quality.

Managed Care and Competition

As this decade progresses, physician executives and hospitals will become central to vertically and horizontally integrated systems. Imagine a world where more than 90 percent of all physician and hospital reimbursement is through capitated payment, where providers bear the risk. It will become necessary to monitor such indicators as access, because "under care" is a concern. Other indicators include admissions per thousand enrollees per year; both inpatient and outpatient utilization rates; missed diagnoses, such as advanced carcinoma of the cervix, breast, or colon; hospital days per thousand contract lives per year; the proportion of the health system's expenses devoted to charity care (if we are to maintain a not-for-profit status); and numbers of low-birthweight babies. For example, a hospital in North Carolina, with a risk-bearing contract for a large Medicaid population, has begun feeding young mothers at high risk of malnutrition and, therefore, of delivery of premature infants; its motive is to reduce or avoid very expensive care for preemies through prevention.

Resource utilization in the outpatient setting has not been studied or managed well by most physician executives. This will become essential in order to reduce the number of services per episode of care without compromising quality. Enrollee satisfaction surveys will be important. Most observers believe that early contracting under managed competition will be largely based on price, because our measures of quality are still primitive. As we begin to build and analyze the ever-enlarging databases necessary to do business in the future, and as all surviving providers become lean and low-priced, quality will be a discriminator in the marketplace and will become a bargaining chip in contract negotiations.

There is early evidence that satisfaction of enrollees in managed care is already a factor. Some employers have switched contracts when employees were displeased with care and access. Enrollee health; waiting time for referrals; continuity, through access to the usual provider; and preventable acute episodes, such as asthmatics arriving in emergency departments or being admitted to the hospital, patients with diabetic ketoacidosis or insulin shock, and hospital-acquired aspiration pneumonia in frail patients who have not been adequately assessed for their ability to either swallow or speak will be but a few of the parameters to track.

Resource Utilization and Futile Care

Resource utilization near the end of life is constantly on the minds of both the public and health care providers. Physician executives will need information to engage health care providers and the community in the ongoing dialogue on this subject. For example, the medical staff in one of the hospitals in the Bon Secours Health System passed a ruling that when a patient in the intensive care unit stays longer than seven days or generates a hospital bill of more than $100,000, an automatic ethics committee consultation is called to help the patient, the family, and the caregiver address the issue of futility. Real-time financial and utilization data will become increasingly useful in the daily work of the physician executive.

Community Health Indicators

As large, integrated health care systems become the responsible entities under health care reform, it will be necessary to have demographic information (including health and disease) and psychographic information (the needs, wants, and concerns of the community) in order to understand and affect the health status of the communities we serve. Health promotion programs and disease prevention indicators, such as immunization and health screening rates, will also be part of this enlarging database. Medical managers should develop and maintain these databases and take the lead in community health enhancement program development.

Risk Management and the Physician Executive

Increasingly, physician executives are at the center of risk management activities in hospitals and health systems. Tracking and trending of complaints, occurrence reports, claims, suits, and settlements of medical malpractice claims have become yet another data source rich in opportunities for improvement in the quality of care and for protection of institutions' resources and images. Most risk management programs have been reactive to events. Workers' compensation claims and payments are rapidly overtaking general and professional liability as major consumers of valuable hospital dollars. With sophisticated data systems to track and trend incidents endangering patients, visitors, and providers, the physician executive can influence outcomes of care while protecting the assets and the image of the health care facility or system.

Integration of Health Care Systems

As integrated health systems mature beyond courtship and early marriage, information will need to flow seamlessly among all the players. Physicians, hospitals, long-term care facilities, payers, other integration partners, home health agencies, etc. will need to share data.

It is likely that, within this decade, we will have a nearly all electronic medical record, with access at all points of service by those with a need to know the information. Utilization of resources can be tracked on a real-time basis as good data management systems are married to clinical pathways. This will allow individual practitioners to become more prudent buyers of supplies and service, and physician executives must be at the center of development and implementation of these data systems.

Practicing physicians and physician leaders must have data at their fingertips. Data must be easily accessed in the hospital, in the office, and from home. The data must include dictated information electronically available within an hour, including, at a minimum, histories and physicals, consultation notes, emergency department and operative notes, discharge summaries, selected radiographic images, electrocardiographs, and real-time physiologic data from critical care units.

From Quality to Value

It is often stated in management that "hard drives out soft." The "hard" pressure we are experiencing to reduce costs will relegate quality to a minor position unless clinical leaders lead. The proper balance of quality and cost will result in value to the individual patient and to those who pay the bills.

$$\text{Value} = \frac{\text{Quality (Perceived and Actual)}}{\text{Price} + \text{Acquisition Costs to Customer}}$$

Successful health care alliances of the future, through good outcomes data, customer satisfaction surveys, systems and process performance data, and financial and other data, will be able to establish their value and thereby win contracts and stay in business.

In the era of reform, hospital physician executives must participate actively in the design, implementation, and maintenance of the health care information highway.

References

1. *Darling v. Charleston Community Memorial Hospital,* 211 NE2d, 253, 1965.

2. *Gonzales v. Nork* No. 228 566 (Cal. Super Ct., Sacramento Co.)(1974).

3. Donabedian, A. "The Evaluation of Medical Care Programs." *Bulletin of the New York Academy of Medicine* 44(2):117-24, Feb. 1968.

4. Craddick, J. "The Medical Management Analysis System: A Professional Liability Warning Mechanism." *Quality Review Bulletin* 5(4):2-8, April 1979.

5. Wennberg, J., and Gittlesohn, A. "Variations in Medical Care among Small Areas." *Scientific American* 246(4):120-34, April 1973.

CHAPTER 7

Performance Measurement: The Joint Commission's Perspective

by Paul M. Schyve, MD

M easuring performance in health care organizations is central both to improving performance and to meeting the growing public demand for information about provider performance. For both these reasons, performance measurement is emphasized in Joint Commission on Accreditation of Healthcare Organization accreditation standards and is the primary focus of its Indicator Measurement System (IMSystem).[1]

The Joint Commission is a nongovernment, not-for-profit organization, founded by health care professionals, whose mission is to improve the quality of care provided to the public. It is governed by a 28-member Board of Commissioners that includes the perspectives of physicians, nurses, health care provider organizations, and the public. The Commission's contribution to improving the quality of care is accomplished through:

- *Measurement* of health care organizations' performance.

- *Evaluation* of these measurements to discern good performance.

- Issuance of *accreditation* decisions to publicly recognize good performance and to indicate the likelihood—although obviously not a guarantee—of future good performance.

While these measurement-evaluation-accreditation activities are themselves designed to foster and guide improvement in the performance of accredited organizations, the Joint Commission also provides education and consultation to assist organizations in their improvement efforts.

At the core, therefore, of the Joint Commission's work is *measurement*. Traditionally, this measurement has been based on measuring compliance with standards. But, in 1985, the Commission recognized that the day was approaching in which the evaluation of a health care organization's performance—and any resulting prediction about its future performance—would not be credible if it did not also take into account the actual results the organization had achieved—specifically, patient health outcomes. It was this realization that led the Commission's Board to make the development of a national performance measurement database, which included patient health outcomes, one of the centerpieces of the Joint Commission's Agenda for Change. This developmental effort resulted in the introduction in 1994 of IMSystem. While the system is initially available on a voluntary basis for hospitals, the intent, over the next few years, is to incorporate into IMSystem appropriate measures for all the other types of health care organizations that the Joint Commission evaluates: ambulatory care, home care, long-term care, mental health care and mental retardation/developmental disabilities organizations, clinical laboratories, and integrated health care networks.

Because the genesis of the system is to enhance the usefulness—and predictive power—of the Joint Commission's measurement, evaluation, and accreditation activities, from the beginning the expectation was that performance measures must, in time, be an integrated part of the accreditation process itself—and, therefore, that all accredited organizations would participate in a performance measurement system, such as IMSystem. In fact, early on, there was speculation that a good performance measurement system based on outcomes could eventually replace the need for standards and on-site surveys. We now realize that there will continue to be a need for standards and on-site surveys even when outcomes measures are available. This issue is discussed below in the section on "Types of Measurement."

When the Joint Commission began development of IMSystem in 1986, it was assumed that relevant, reliable, valid outcomes measures could be pulled off the shelf—that the basic work had already been done. Soon the sobering truth became evident: There were few, if any, such tested performance measures available. Hospitals, for example, were infrequently measuring their performance with respect to outcomes—with some exceptions, such as infection rates and inhospital mortality. But even these measurement exceptions usually had not been evaluated with regard to reliability or validity, nor were the measures risk-adjusted to permit useful comparisons among hospitals. The Joint Commission, having determined that a national system of performance measures was necessary, found itself the developer of not only a system and measures, but even of the methodology for their development. In the intervening years, other performance measurement systems have been developed. In early 1995, the Joint Commission issued an invitation to other measurement systems to collaborate with the Joint Commission in providing performance measurements for the accreditation process. Many systems responded positively, and the Joint Commission has appointed a National Council on Performance Measurement to establish criteria for choosing measurement systems, for evaluating the systems against the criteria, and for recommending systems that should be eligible for use in the accreditation process. Accredited organizations would be able to choose among the eligible systems to meet the performance measurement needs of the future accreditation process.

This chapter outlines some of the key issues and assumptions that underlie the Commission's approach to performance measurement systems in accredited health care organizations. While many of these issues and assumptions were identified by or learned from others, they also include many that are derived from the Commission's sometimes painful experience in developing IMSystem.

Performance

Performance in health care is what is done and how well it is done. Performance leads to *results*, including patient health outcomes (broadly defined to include physiological status, functional status, physical and psychological comfort, and prevention), satisfaction with health care, and the costs or resource use associated with the care. Patients and others consider these results, and the manner in which the care was provided, as they make *judgments* about the quality and, when costs are included, the *value* of the health care.

Performance Measures

A performance measure is any unit, or quantitative tool using the unit, for measuring the level of performance of individuals, organizations, or comprehensive networks of health care.[2] Performance measures in health care include measures of processes (what is done and how it is done) and of results (patient health outcomes, satisfaction, and costs). The Joint Commission calls these performance measures "indicators" of quality, because they are not direct measures of quality. Rather, they are measures of the processes and outcomes that various individuals and groups use in making their own, often idiosyncratic, judgments about quality. But it is these processes and, to some extent, outcomes that are under the control of the health care organization and, therefore, should be the foci of its improvement efforts. Changing what the organization *can* control is the route to influencing judgments about the quality of its services.

Purpose of Performance Measurement

All good performance measurements should be designed to produce data that are useful in decision making. But even good raw measurement *data* must usually first be assessed or evaluated in order to yield *information* that can be used to answer important questions or to make decisions. The questions or decisions may be internal to the health care organization. For example, where are there opportunities for improvement? Of the many opportunities, which have the highest priorities? What changes are most likely to lead to improvement? Did these changes actually result in improvement?

The questions or decisions may also be external to the organization. For example, if there is more than one health care organization that provides the health care services I need, which would be my best choice for the future, i.e., which will provide good, safe care? Of the many organizations offering care, which should be authorized to receive payment in the future? These decisions may be made by consumers or patients; by purchasers of health care, such as employers; by payers, such as insurance companies; or by government bodies, such as state licensure agencies, among others.

Dimensions of Performance

These decisions, whether internal or external to the organization, are often based on data from measurements that relate to nine dimensions of performance. While descriptions of these dimensions are couched here in clinical terms, they apply to all types of processes, including governance, managerial, and support processes in health care organizations.

Two of these dimensions relate to "what" is done: the *efficacy* of a specific test, procedure, treatment, or service in relation to an illness or condition, and the *appropriateness* of a specific test, procedure, treatment, or service to meet a specific patient's needs. Efficacy is a measurement of the degree to which a treatment is known to work for certain conditions or situations; appropriateness is a measurement of the degree to which the treatment is right for a specific patient, in light of his or her condition.

The other seven dimensions relate to "how well" the "what" is done: the *availability* of a needed test, procedure, treatment, or service to the patient who needs it; the *timeliness* with which a needed test, procedure, treatment, or service is provided to the patient, i.e., whether it is provided within the time frame in which it will be most useful; the *effectiveness*, or technical correctness, with which a test, procedure, treatment, or service is provided; the *continuity* over time of the services provided to the patient with respect to other services, practitioners, and providers; the *safety* of the patient to whom the service is provided and of others; the *efficiency* with which the service is provided, i.e., the use of resources, including equipment and supplies, money, information, and people in providing the service; and the *respect and caring* with which the service is provided.

These dimensions are not independent of each other. For example, use of a nonefficacious therapy will preclude appropriateness; if a treatment is not provided in a timely manner, its effectiveness will be compromised; and availability will obviously affect timeliness. (In fact, when availability and timeliness are combined, they are often referred to as "access.") Yet each dimension can be defined separately. An example may help clarify the differences among efficacy, appropriateness, and effectiveness. The physician wants *efficacious* medications in the formulary: antibiotics that work, rather than those that don't or have unnecessary risks associated with their use. The physician wants to use the *appropriate* antibiotic for the patient: one to which the organism infecting the patient is sensitive and to which the patient is not allergic. And the physician wants to use the antibiotic *effectively*: in the correct dose, route, and frequency; over the correct time span; and with the correct monitoring of results.

Any measure of a process or result will usually provide data about performance relative to one or more of these nine dimensions.

Types of Measurement

Performance measures yield data that answer questions about past levels of performance—how often was a process used, what outcomes were achieved? If questions to be answered based on the resulting data require only knowledge of the current and past state of affairs (e.g., how many total hip replacements were done last year and what was their average cost?), *enumerative* studies based on the performance measures are appropriate. In an enumerative study, the intent is to draw inferences by sampling from a well-defined existing population, all the members of which can (at least in theory) be enumerated.

However, many of the most important questions and decisions facing a health care organization (e.g., which changes are most likely to lead to improvement?) or patients or purchasers (e.g., will this organization provide good care in the future?) require an ability to predict future performance. In some cases, such a prediction is based on the assumption that the underlying processes will not change: for example, "If the hospital continues to do total hip replacements in the same way as it did last year, what are the likely outcomes this year?" In other cases, the prediction involves an assumption that the processes will change: for example, "If the hospital has the physical therapist visit the patient at home before admission, will it result in more rapid return to independent mobilization after total hip replacement?" These decisions require *analytic* studies, in which predictions about future performance are made even though available measurements are of past performance.

To predict the future performance of an organization based on its past performance, it is important to know whether the organization has systematically designed patient care processes (e.g., patient assessment and patient education) and organizational processes (e.g., management of human resources and of information) to be stable and systematically measures its performance to identify variation. Identification of undesirable variation and taking of action to restore stability are based on statistical process control and are reflected in the *new* quality assurance—i.e., measurement of performance of processes and, based on an understanding of the causes of variation, reduction in the underlying special or common causes for any undesirable variation. (This contrasts with the *old* quality assurance, which focused primarily on individual performance and used interventions that often bore no relationship to processes or to an understanding of the underlying causes of variation.)

Certainly in health care, it is not enough to continue to produce yesterday's outcomes. The state of knowledge and available technology is constantly changing—along with the expectations of patients and other customers—and the organization must continually improve its performance. It must move beyond even the new quality assurance into *continuous improvement*. The organization with the best outcomes today and with stable processes to maintain them in the future will, nevertheless, fall behind if it does not systematically improve what it does and how well it does it—i.e., its performance.

Therefore, one of the most powerful tools in analytic studies is knowledge as to whether the organization consistently conforms to state-of-the-art specifications for the performance of basic patient care and organization management processes. These specifications can be called "standards." There are, then, two types of measures that are important in evaluating and managing the performance of a health care organization— *performance measures* and *conformance to standards*. Performance measures quantify the past performance of the health care organization. Measures of conformance to state-of-the-art standards for important basic patient care and organizational processes (such as those identified as important "functions" in the 1995 *Accreditation Manual for Hospitals*[3] and the 1994 *Accreditation Manual for Health Care Networks*[4]) quantify how well the organization systematically designs and attends to what it does and how it does it. Measures of conformance to specific standards that focus on the new quality assurance and on continuous improvement quantify how well the organization maintains stability when appropriate and how well it changes and improves performance when possible. It is the combination of good past performance (i.e., outcomes) and good conformance with state-of-the-art standards that provides the data for analytic studies that try to predict good patient outcomes in the future. In the face of poor conformance to state-of-the-art standards, even good past performance is not sufficient to inspire confidence that the future outcomes will be good. Both types of measures are vital, and each is complementary to the other.

In addition, good past outcomes for specific treatments or diagnoses, combined with conformance to state-of-the-art clinical practice guidelines for those treatments or diagnoses, are more likely to predict good future outcomes than if the guidelines are ignored. For this reason, Joint Commission standards on improving organizational performance specifically reference the need to use good clinical practice guidelines in the design, and improvement, of clinical processes.

Scope of Measurement

In designing a useful performance measurement system, the first question to be addressed is *why* is measurement necessary? That is, what are the anticipated uses for the measurement system—what are the questions to be answered by the system, and what decisions are to be based upon the data and the information the data will yield? What do the system's users need? The answer to the *why* will help determine *what* specifically is to be measured.

The potential users of performance measures include clinical practitioners, health care organizations, the public, purchasers, payers, accrediting bodies, government regulators, public policy makers, and health services researchers. These groups have some questions and decisions in common, and some that may be unique to their own interests and responsibilities. Nevertheless, the more the Joint Commission has explored with various groups their decision-making responsibilities and the performance measurement data they believe would assist them, the more similar the scope of the desired measures has become. This scope includes the following five categories of performance measures:

- Clinical performance, especially with respect to high-volume and high-cost procedures and treatments. Clinical performance includes the prevention, early detection, appropriateness of management, and effectiveness of management of the clinical conditions of specific patient populations, whether defined by age, by diagnosis, by DRG, by procedure, etc.

- Health status. Health status can be measured for patients served, for enrolled populations, or even for geographically defined communities.

- Satisfaction with the services provided.

- Efficiency and effectiveness of the organization's processes (e.g., managing information, credentialing, financial management).

- Communications to and education of the population served and the providers responsible for carrying out these communications and education.

To help health care organizations determine the specific measures they should use, the Joint Commission designed a "quality cube" (see figure on page 55). The cube emphasizes that the specific measures to be used in evaluating a health care organization's performance should be balanced, focused, and comprehensive in scope. This balance, focus, and comprehensiveness can be achieved if three different perspectives on the

Measuring Clinical Care: A Guide for Physician Executives

THE QUALITY CUBE

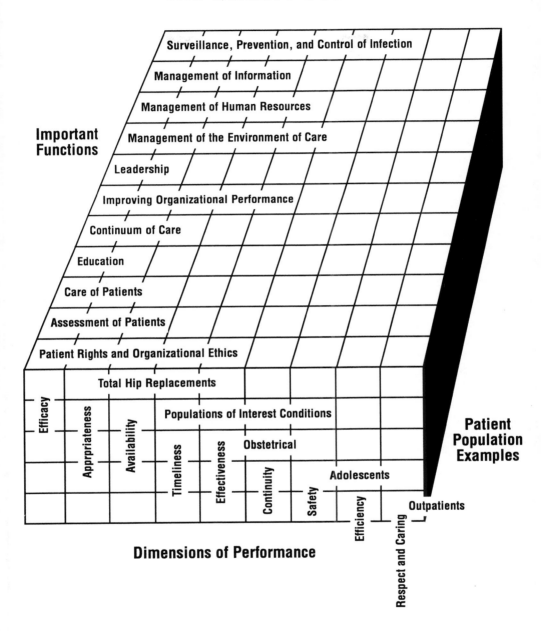

Important Functions

- Surveillance, Prevention, and Control of Infection
- Management of Information
- Management of Human Resources
- Management of the Environment of Care
- Leadership
- Improving Organizational Performance
- Continuum of Care
- Education
- Care of Patients
- Assessment of Patients
- Patient Rights and Organizational Ethics

Patient Population Examples

- Total Hip Replacements
- Populations of Interest Conditions
- Obstetrical
- Adolescents
- Outpatients

Dimensions of Performance

- Efficacy
- Apprpriateness
- Availability
- Timeliness
- Effectiveness
- Continuity
- Safety
- Efficiency
- Respect and Caring

organization's performance are integrated. The first perspective focuses on those important governance, managerial, clinical, and support functions—or systems and processes—in the organization that have the greatest impact on patient health outcomes. These functions, such as assessment of patients and management of information, are depicted on the top face of the cube. They correspond to the chapter titles in the 1995 *Accreditation Manual for Hospitals*[3] and, by 1996, in all of the other Joint Commission accreditation manuals.

The second perspective focuses on the nine dimensions of performance described above, such as efficiency and appropriateness (see "Dimensions of Performance"). These dimensions are depicted on the front face of the cube.

The third perspective focuses on the clinical care provided to specific patient populations, such as total hip replacement patients and obstetrical patients. These patient populations are depicted on the side face of the cube.

Clinical care for specific patient populations and dimensions of performance—a two-dimensional matrix composed of the cube's side and front faces—correspond primarily to the first category of desired measures listed above, i.e., those related to "clinical performance." Choosing appropriate measures in this category of data entails selecting the priority patient populations (e.g., patients undergoing a specific procedure, patients with a specific diagnosis) and the dimensions of performance most relevant to the clinical care of those populations. This category of measures corresponds quite closely to many of the sets of indicators developed over the past seven years by the Joint Commission for IMSystem—indicators for perioperative, obstetrical, trauma, oncology, and cardiovascular care.

The cube's top face—important functions—corresponds primarily to the fourth and fifth categories of measures, those relevant to the efficiency and effectiveness of the organization's processes, including those related to communications and education. These categories are primarily based on measuring compliance with standards for important systems and processes in the organization, including standards such as those in the "Patient-Focused Functions" and "Organizational Functions" sections of the 1995 *Accreditation Manual for Hospitals.*[3]

Thus, while care to specific patient populations and dimensions of performance are primarily assessed through performance measures, the organization's important functions are primarily assessed through measures of standards compliance. As discussed above (see "Types of Measurement"), measures of compliance with standards for important systems and processes are combined with performance measures to help predict the future performance of the organization. Again, using performance measures alone provides an incomplete perspective on which to base predictions of future performance.

Levels of Measurement

Data for the five categories of measures described above (see "Scope of Measurement") can be collected at several levels in the health care delivery system: the individual practitioner's office; the health care organization, such as hospital, nursing home, clinic, or home care agency; the health care network, composed of multiple practitioners and organizations that are integrated into a delivery network; or a geopolitically defined population (e.g., city, state, country).

For the data to be useful in decision making—whether for internal improvement or for external purposes—measures should be applied, and data collected and reported, at the level of the delivery system that can be held *accountable* for the measured performance. That is, there must be an entity, such as an individual, a hospital, or a network, that has the power to change the measured performance and is, therefore, accountable for the performance.

For some measures, data can be aggregated or "rolled up" from one level of the delivery system to the next higher level. An example would be the aggregation of complication rates for a surgical procedure at each hospital in a network to calculate the complication rate for the network as a whole. In other measures of performance of a higher level organization, such as a network, the measure cannot be derived from aggregated performance of component entities. An example would be a measure of network enrollees' current knowledge as to how to obtain services when outside the network's geographic area.

Conversely, disaggregating data to components of a larger organization may lead to invalid conclusions about the components' performance. For example, attributing outcomes solely to individual practitioners for care provided in a complex organizational setting such as a hospital is problematic. In such complex organizations, patient outcomes are heavily influenced by the organization's systems and processes, in addition to the individual practitioner's knowledge, skill, and judgment. Thus, while comparisons of performance among practitioners within a hospital can be useful—because systems and processes are more likely to be similar for all the practitioners—comparisons among individual practitioners across different hospitals are likely to be misleading.

Characteristics of Good Measures

Having determined what to measure and the level of the health care system to which the identified measures should be applied, the measurer has an obligation to ensure that the measures to be used are good ones.

Criteria for good measures are significance, cost-effectiveness, variation, linkage to health outcomes, reliability, and validity. *Significance* refers to the selection of measures that are both relevant (i.e., meaningful measures of performance) and of high enough priority (e.g., based on volume, risk, or cost of care) to justify investing in data collection, analysis, dissemination, and use. *Cost-effectiveness* of a measure is the usefulness of the measure in relation to the cost of its application. *Variation* refers to whether the measure has the ability to discriminate between organizations when used for purposes of comparison. *Linkage to health outcomes* refers to the ability of a process measure to serve as a proxy for a likely outcome (e.g., mammography rates serving as a proxy for diagnosis of breast cancer at an early stage, which is related to the likelihood of successful treatment).

Reliability refers to the accuracy and completeness of the data, and their reproducibility by different measurers and over time. Within an organization, the accuracy and reproducibility of a measure depend in part on the clarity and specificity of the definitions of the data elements that the measure comprises, and the completeness depends on the methods for data recording and collection. For measures collected from multiple organizations, reliability also depends on the uniformity across organizations of data element definitions and of the methods for recording, collecting, and transmitting data. In the development of IMSystem, the Joint Commission invested heavily in the development of precise data dictionaries and in the measurement of the reliability both of the data elements and of the overall indicator rates (e.g., through reabstraction of patient-specific data elements on-site in hospitals and recalculation of indicator rates).

Validity refers to whether measures measure what they are intended to measure—in this case, performance. Although it has various technical definitions, validity is ultimately measured by the likelihood that a decision based on the data is correct; for example, a decision that patient outcomes can be improved by a change in the process is borne out in practice, or, when people decide to have surgery at hospital X rather than hospital Y, they have better outcomes than like patients who went to hospital Y. Measuring this ultimate validity is complex. Measurement depends, of course, on the relevance of the measure, the reliability with which its data are collected, and its risk adjustment (see below). But ultimate validity also depends on the skill of the user in transforming the measure into information and in using that information to make logical and correct decisions. Finally, establishing ultimate validity usually requires measurement over time (for example, of outcomes).

Because of the complexity in measuring ultimate validity, validity is often established in stages. The usual first stage is face validity: Does the measure seem relevant and meaningful to experts and to health care professionals in the field who are the actual users of the measure and the resulting data? The second stage assesses the degree to which health care professionals perceive that variation in the measure identifies opportunities for improvement. The third stage assesses the degree to which action is taken on the basis of this perception, and the fourth stage assesses the degree to which these actions result in improvement that can be reflected by the measures. In beta testing of indicators during the development of IMSystem, the first and second stages of validity testing were completed, and partial data were collected—and continue to be collected—for the third and fourth stages, which, obviously, require longer follow-up and are more dependent on the knowledge and resources of the health care organizations.

Comparative Information

Many important decisions are and will be made using information that compares one organization's performance with that of others. The organization itself may use such comparisons to formulate questions that stimulate improvement activities, such as: Do other hospitals get better patient outcomes after total hip replacements than our hospital does? If so, do they perform the procedure differently?

The Joint Commission will use comparisons derived from IMSystem and other eligible measurement systems when they become part of the accreditation process (probably in 1997) to focus its external evaluation process, asking a series of questions such as: Does a hospital have more surgical site infections than expected, based on the risk-adjusted rates of surgical site infections in other hospitals? Does the hospital recognize this difference and use the information to set priorities for further assessment? Does the hospital understand why it has higher rates? If the hospital is accountable for the higher rates, does it take action to improve the rates? If the hospital does not recognize the differences, or is unable to understand their cause, or takes no action when action is possible, is the hospital out of compliance with Joint Commission standards for important related systems and processes?

Finally, it is clear that the public intends to use performance data to compare organizations to make decisions such as: Which health care network should I join? Which hospital should I go to?

Risk Adjustment

If data will be used by health care organizations and the public to make decisions, the reliability and validity of the data must be known. But reliable and valid data are not sufficient. Useful and fair comparisons of performance among organizations—especially with respect to outcomes—require that the data from each organization be adjusted for factors that are beyond the organization's control. Most such factors relate to patients, including differences in the severity of patients' illnesses at admission; differences in the existence of other diseases the patients have (comorbid conditions); biological variations (e.g., age, sex) among patients; differences in patients' preferences and consent for treatment; differences in patients' involvement in the treatment process, including patients' "compliance" with treatment plans; and other patient-related differences, such as socioeconomic level or exposure to environmental toxins. The more the data can be adjusted for these patient-related factors, the greater degree to which the comparisons among organizations are likely to reflect true differences in organization performance.

The adjustment process—"risk adjustment"—can vary in complexity (see Chapter 10). One method is to adjust aggregated patient outcomes for an organization, based on an aggregate measure of risk factors (e.g., adjusting a hospital's observed mortality for myocardial infarction, CABGs, and PTCAs downward because its patients, on the average, are older). In reality, however, the actual risk factors and their relative weights vary according to the outcome being measured. For example, while age is a relevant risk factor in adjusting rates of mortality for both CABGs and PTCAs, it may weigh more heavily—or in a different pattern, such as linear versus parabolic—in one than the other. Therefore, an ideal risk adjustment system should:

- Use a different set of variables, with different weights for each variable (based on both their individual contributions and their interactions), for each performance measure.

- Adjust each patient's data for each performance measure separately.

- Take the average of patients' adjusted data to calculate an adjusted rate for each performance measure for the organization as a whole.

This sophisticated approach to risk adjustment, employed by the Joint Commission in IMSystem, can only be applied if the aggregate database contains patient-level data. That is, indicator-specific risk adjustment cannot be carried out if organizations contributing to the database provide only rates on performance measures (e.g., the mortality rate for CABGs) and rates of risk-adjustment factors (e.g., the age distribution of the patient population). Rather, each organization must contribute relevant data elements for each patient, as is required in IMSystem.

One could argue that a method that adequately adjusts for patient-specific risk factors should obviate the need for any groupings of health care organizations as the initial basis for comparison using such variables as urban/rural location, teaching status, or size. Nonetheless, because the data per se cannot be directly translated into quality, such groupings are a matter of interest for many health care organizations and probably will need to be taken into account in any full-scale public release of performance data. Thus, while IMSystem routinely provides to each organization risk-adjusted comparisons to the entire population of participating similar organization (e.g., hospitals), both individual and group requests for segmented comparisons (e.g., by size) will be accommodated when the database is of sufficient size.

Finally, because it is rarely, if ever, possible to fully adjust for all of the factors that are beyond the health care organization's control, even risk-adjusted comparisons should be interpreted cautiously. That is, the decision maker should ask the question, "Why are these performance data different among organizations?" To answer this question requires an analysis of the data and often more information than the data alone can provide. Within the organization, it may require more measurement and assessment, including peer review. External to the organization, it may require asking the organization or a patient's physician to explain the differences.

Risk-adjustment methods can be costly. For each adjustment factor, one or more additional data elements must be collected, and each data element collected has some associated cost. Elements that are currently collected for some other purpose (most commonly for billing) create no new cost other than the cost of moving them into a new electronic file. Unfortunately, there is little or no uniformity among payers in the sets of data that they require on each patient for billing purposes, and sometimes payers use inconsistent definitions of data elements or inconsistent electronic file formats. This problem is further aggravated when nonpayer stakeholders (e.g., government agencies, business coalitions) wish to collect and utilize data that may be different from those used by any of the payers. And there has been extensive documentation of the high rates of inaccuracy in billing data.

The investment in the risk-adjustment approach depends in part on the importance and effects of decisions to be based on the data. Therefore, the selection of variables to be collected for risk adjustment is always a compromise among the burden on the organization of collecting a specific data element accurately and completely; the magnitude of the contribution of the data element to the adequacy of the risk adjustment; the risk that a performance measure will be misinterpreted or misused, especially by others, such as patients and payers, without the specific adjustment permitted by collecting data for the additional variable; and the effect and cost of erroneous decisions that may result from misinterpretation or misuse.

The Joint Commission has attempted to reach a judicious compromise in developing IMSystem. A major objective for this system has been to moderate, and potentially even reduce, organizational costs for data collection by being selective in what performance measures (i.e., indicators) to use; being parsimonious in the selection of data elements that must be collected, including those needed for risk adjustment; and attempting to permit use of already existing data elements (e.g., ICD-9-CM codes, UB-92 data) to the extent possible. To the degree that collaboration between the Joint Commission and other measurement systems can be used as a vehicle for achieving consensus on the measures and data elements to be used by multiple parties for assessing the performance of health care organizations, the administrative and cost burdens of data collection will be significantly reduced.

Use of Performance Measures

Health care organizations are concerned and sometimes confused about the potential uses of performance information. While external uses—and misuses—are a reasonable concern, perhaps the most critical issue is internal use, as a managerial tool to stimulate and support quality improvement, of information that compares the organization's performance to that of other organizations. If the data collected, and the reports received, are not useful to the organization, there can be little justification for the costs incurred in collecting these data.

The use of risk-adjusted comparative data as the initial basis for improvement efforts requires an understanding that health care is a set of processes and that there is normal variation in processes. The recognition that health care is a set of processes helps to identify the clinicians and other staff (and the departments in the organization) who must work together to achieve the desired outcomes and their improvement. Recognition that the causes of variation may be built into a process (common causes) or may be extrinsic to a process (special causes) is critical to taking the right action to reduce variation or to improve a process' performance and its outcome. Assessment of performance data to turn them into useful information is facilitated by knowledge of statistical analysis tools (e.g., run charts, control charts) and process analysis tools (e.g., flow charts, cause-effect diagrams). (See Chapter 13). Often overlooked is the need to understand the difference between enumerative studies (of what is or has been) and analytic studies (designed to predict the future), as discussed in "Types of Measurement."

All this knowledge and these tools are of little use if the comparative data do not get to the individuals who are interested in using the data and who have the knowledge and ability to design and make changes for improvement. In the Joint Commission's beta testing experience during development of IMSystem, there was great diversity among hospitals in their use of the beta feedback reports, which compare each hospital's performance to that of other participating hospitals. Some hospitals regularly distributed the reports to multiple internal audiences and found them to be quite useful. Others neither distributed them nor found them useful as a tool for quality improvement. Understanding these differences in behavior and opinions and addressing both the organizational factors that influence the perceived value of the data and the data system factors (such as report format) that influence their use are essential to maximizing the value of the investment made in any data collection effort.

The Future of Performance Measurement

The measurement of performance is at the heart of continuous improvement.[5] Managing these data and information well is of particular importance in improving the processes and outcomes of health care.[6] And often these data and information are of greatest help when placed in a comparative context. This is the rationale behind the Joint Commission's creation of IMSystem. Our desire is for a relevant, reliable, useful (valid), and cost-effective system. For this reason, the Joint Commission's goal is establishment of a nationally uniform performance measurement system that uses the best measures available—whether developed at the Joint Commission or elsewhere.

While it is true that, when the Joint Commission began development of the system in 1986, few others were developing or testing such performance measures, now many are. The IMSystem of the future will draw on relevant measures of known reliability and validity wherever the source. The system opened in January 1994 with 10 tested (and subsequently refined) performance measures for anesthesia-related perioperative care and obstetrical care; in January 1995, 21 measures in the areas of oncology, trauma, and cardiovascular care were added. Eleven more measures in the areas of infection control and medication use will be added in January 1996.

A national performance measurement system that is useful for hospitals also should be useful to other types of health care organizations and to networks of organizations. Consequently, the Joint Commission has initiated collaboration with other developers and testers of performance measures to identify the best measures in various areas to incorporate in IMSystem. In early 1995, a Request for Indicators (RFI) was issued to identify performance measures for health care networks, and a national expert Indicator Advisory Group will select from measures submitted for inclusion in IMSystem. Future RFIs will be issued for other types of accredited organizations and their services (e.g., long-term care, home care, pediatric care). The goal is to develop an IMSystem "menu" of performance measures from which an organization can choose on the basis of the services it provides, its location and size, and its own improvement priorities.

As measures are improved, and as we all—practitioners, health care organizations and networks, accrediting bodies, patients and consumers, payers and purchasers—learn to use measurement effectively and efficiently for improvement purposes and to make other decisions, the importance of nationally uniform databases such as that of IMSystem will grow. And as we attempt to predict future performance based on the data in these databases, the relationship of outcomes measures to compliance with state-of-the-art organizational standards and good practice guidelines will become more evident.

References

1. *The Measurement Mandate*. Oakbrook Terrace, Ill.: Joint Commission on Accreditation of Healthcare Organizations, 1990.

2. O'Leary, M. *Lexikon: Dictionary of Health Care Terms, Organizations and Acronyms for the Era of Reform*. Oakbrook Terrace, Ill.: Joint Commission on Accreditation of Healthcare Organizations, 1994, p.454.

3. *1995 Accreditation Manual for Hospitals*. Oakbrook Terrace, Ill.: Joint Commission on Accreditation of Healthcare Organizations, 1994.

4. *1994 Accreditation Manual for Health Care Networks*. Oakbrook Terrace, Ill.: Joint Commission on Accreditation of Healthcare Organizations, 1994.

5. "A Framework for Improving the Performance of Health Care Organizations." *Joint Commission Perspectives* 13(6):A1-6, Nov.-Dec. 1993.

6. Schyve, P., and Kamowski, D. "Information Management and Quality Improvement: The Joint Commission's Perspective. *Quality Management in Health Care* 2(4): 54-62, Summer 1994.

CHAPTER 8

What Information Do Clinicians Need?

by Gordon Mosser, MD

Like everyone else who provides or manages health care, clinicians need information to play their parts in cycles of process design, implementation, performance assessment, and redesign. Unfortunately, most clinicians have not been trained to see themselves as participants in these cycles. For this reason, they often do not want information obtained by measuring clinical care; they see no need for it. Their attention is commonly focused on information about particular patients and their needs.

Part of a health care leader's job, especially the physician executive's, is to create hunger among clinicians for information about clinical care, about the systems in which clinicians work. The starting point for this task is the goal that clinicians already zealously embrace: good care for patients. Starting with this goal as a foundation, the need for systems measurements can be persuasively constructed.

Let us begin with a framework for performance assessment to be reported to clinicians. What kinds of measurements would be useful to clinicians? A simple trio of categories will serve us well, because it is easily remembered and yet comprehensive[1]:

- Technical performance.

- Service.

- Efficiency.

"Technical performance" refers to excellence in the prevention, diagnosis, and treatment of disease. This component of performance is, of course, what physicians and the public in general ordinarily have in mind when they speak of the quality of health care—when they say, for example, that the United States has the best medical care in the world. Technical performance, in turn, can be explained by considering four objects of measurement:

- Health care processes.

- Intermediate health care effects.

- Morbidity and mortality.

- Patient-assessed outcomes.

These objects or targets of measurement are listed in order of decreasing proximity to care givers. Health care processes are directly controlled by care givers. For example, one can measure how frequently women presenting for preventive services have a mammogram ordered when those women are of the right age and have not had a mammogram performed in the prescribed interval.

Next and slightly downstream are measures of intermediate care effects—that is, results that can reasonably be expected to follow from appropriate processes and are desirable, although they are not health outcomes of intrinsic interest. For example, the proportion of new breast cancer cases diagnosed at stage I can be expected to increase if mammograms are appropriately ordered. This increased proportion is not in itself a desirable outcome; it is desirable because it is known to be predictive of reduced morbidity and mortality from breast cancer.

Further downstream are morbidity and mortality measures. These are true endpoints, but they are defined in medical terms, which embody concepts and value judgments that may not be shared by the intended beneficiaries or customers, namely, patients.

Patient-assessed outcomes—that is, outcomes assessed from the patient's point of view—are the final touchstone, the health outcomes of ultimate interest. They include pain relief, restoration of function, avoidance of death, and several others. Medically defined measures of morbidity are legitimate health outcome measurements only insofar as they predict these outcomes or serve as surrogate measures for them. Patient-assessed outcomes are usually measured by asking patients. Of course, lack of knowledge may prevent a patient from accurately assessing whether his or her real interests have been served. Patient-assessed outcomes are best defined as outcomes reported by an idealized, highly knowledgeable patient.

"Service" refers to the process of health care as experienced by patients and their families. It has two components:

- Personal care.

- Access.

Personal care considerations include courtesy, individual attention, genuine listening, and compassion. This dimension can be measured only by patient reports. Access considerations include telephone availability, appointment availability, and waiting times in clinics and other facilities. This dimension is also most reliably measured by direct patient evaluations, because these reports implicitly encompass patients' standards for access. However, surrogate measures can be useful and more practical—for example, counts of days until appointments are available and measurements of how long telephones ring before they are answered.

"Efficiency" refers to minimization of resources used for a given health care effect. Health care services cannot be said to be efficient or inefficient without reference to some assumed outcome or benefit. In the absence of a reference outcome, services can be said only to be inexpensive or expensive. Efficiency is a measure of value, that is, of benefit relative to cost. It is not a measure of cost considered in isolation.[2]

With a general account of the targets of measurement in view, we are positioned to consider the first rule in delivering performance information to clinicians:

Report performance for a service unit that can be influenced by the clinician. In other words, provide information that can be used. The service unit should not be too large. For example, reports on an entire hospital, health plan, or multispecialty group practice are not useful to individual clinicians, because they cannot work to improve performance on the whole and may not even identify with it. Reports on individual clinical sites, care units within large health centers, or operating room teams will be more to the point. (In contrast, reports on entire hospitals or other large units are useful to those who manage those units.) Measurements of individual physicians are ordinarily too narrowly focused to be useful. Very few health care tasks are carried out under the predominant control of an individual physician, because contemporary health care is delivered in teams. A clinician will exert influence to improve performance by functioning as a member of a service unit team. In the design of measurement strategies, service units should be identified by looking to see what is the smallest grouping of providers and support staff that performs self-sufficiently (or nearly so) in carrying out a given task. Measurement for clinicians should be fashioned around these groupings or service units as the units of analysis.

In order for measurements of clinical care to be actionable, of course, the clinician must know whether performance is good or bad. This consideration leads us to the second rule of reporting:

Report measurements relative to a standard that permits evaluation of performance. Purely descriptive reporting is not actionable and generally squanders the time of staff members who prepare the reports. In contrast, three kinds of comparisons provide a basis for evaluation and are useful:

■ Time series of performance measures within one service unit.

■ Comparisons of performance as compared with a benchmark process.

■ Comparisons of similar service units.

Comparisons of measures within a single service unit over time generally provide good value. These measures are usefully presented in the run charts of continuous quality improvement.[3] Interpreted against a background of detailed knowledge about the unit, time series data can permit the unit's members to judge whether they are improving and to assess what is working for improvement and what is not. Comparative data of this kind are at the core of effective improvement efforts.

Time series measurements can be enhanced by comparing actual practice to current best process, that is, by doing a form of benchmarking. Addition of the notion of current best process completes the list of materials needed for full use of the cycle of design, implementation, assessment, and redesign. A best process specification is simply an explicit account of what the service unit wants to do. At any point, this account will be flawed because of imperfect knowledge. Measuring actual performance against the benchmark will lead at times to changes in the activities of care. At other times it will lead to redesign of the process, that is, redefinition of best process because a better one has been discovered. Such repeatedly improved process specifications are in fact health care guidelines at their best: not templates for inspection or punishment, not rule sets for payment, but instead repeatedly improved workplans for service units. Guidelines provide the yardsticks that make evaluation of performance possible, enabling measurements of clinical care to be evaluative and therefore actionable.

Comparative measurement of similar service units is an additional and common reporting strategy, but its usefulness is limited. Its principal use is to raise consciousness, that is, to show clinicians what others are doing and therefore what might be done. Limitations arise from the rarity of truly similar service units. Different units have different patients, different resource ceilings, and different data sources affecting reporting comparability. Even when expensive efforts have been made through severity adjustments and data validation studies, doubt lingers in the clinician's mind. The effort to achieve believable comparability is generally not repaid. Nonetheless, in certain circumstances, comparative reporting of this kind can be eye-opening and highly motivating. These results can be achieved when the compared units recognize each other as truly similar, that is, as genuine peer groups. For example, health centers or clinics within a single staff-model HMO can often be usefully compared with one another, sometimes in considerable detail. Orthopedic or cardiac surgery operating teams can also be usefully compared, as long as the teams themselves see each other as similar.

How, then, should measurements be presented to clinicians to maximize the likelihood that they will be used for improvement? The third rule of reporting is:

Report performance in order to empower decision making. In other words, fashion data collection, analysis, and reporting activities so that they facilitate good decision making and consequent action for improvement. This rule incorporates several considerations:

- Measurement for improvement, not for research or score keeping.

- Timely and frequent reporting.

- Preference for graphical displays.

- Avoidance of formats that are threatening.

- Maximizing motivation.

Measuring for improvement differs from measuring for research. Measuring for improvement means collecting local data for local use. The audience is internal to a given service unit—for example, a clinic, a hospital nursing service, or a medical group. The purpose is to improve care. In contrast, the audience for research measurement is the health care community at large, and the purpose is to contribute to the general body of scientific knowledge. Measurement for research is typically precise, complex, and greatly concerned with confounding variables. Measurement for improvement of a

Measuring Clinical Care: A Guide for Physician Executives

given service unit is typically repetitive, less precise, and simpler. It is less concerned with confounding variables because the users of the information are familiar with the setting and can take most confounders into account without quantitative measurements. Measuring for improvement requires frequent judgments about whether to measure particular potential confounders and, if so, how elaborately to measure them. In measuring for research, a simpler rule holds sway: when in doubt, measure it.

Measuring for improvement also differs from measuring for score keeping. The audience for score keeping is external. It may be purchasers or government regulatory bodies. The purpose of score keeping is to provide a basis for choice or to deliver on an obligation to be accountable—or at times to reassure. Measurement for score keeping is typically highly summarized. Comparison of different service organizations is central to its purpose. For this reason, it is much concerned with achieving comparability. Measurement for improvement provides greater detail about processes so that service units can improve or redesign their activities. It provides less detail pertinent to comparisons across service units, for example, measures used for severity adjustment. It avoids presenting comparisons that are demoralizing. Measurement for score keeping is pursued independently of any motivational effects on the service units.

To be useful for improvement, reporting must be timely. Reports on performance one or two years ago are rarely motivating. Ordinarily, data should be presented within two or three months of the events that were measured. These events will be of interest because they reflect the consequences of actions taken for improvement. The time interval between the actions taken and the measured effects should also be short, not more than a few months. The need for timeliness rules out the use of many otherwise attractive measures of morbidity, mortality, and patient-assessed outcomes. If the elapsed time between cause and effect is more than a few months, measurements of the effect will have diminished power for quality improvement. Studies of cause and effect over longer intervals are entirely appropriate as research, and the research results, in turn, can be used to ground quality improvement efforts. In other words, once research has shown a causal connection between a process step and a long-term outcome of intrinsic interest, the process step (or a short-term effect of it) can be used as the focus of measurement for quality improvement.

Incidentally, measuring for improvement with an intention to publish is likely to interfere with improvement efforts, even if the interval between cause and effect is short. The complexity of measurement for a general scientific audience usually slows down the process, diminishing the data's motivational power, because data delivery occurs later than would be desirable for process improvement purposes.

Measurements for improvement should also be presented frequently in order to maintain the momentum of the project at hand. Suitable intervals range from weekly to semi-annually. Annual reports will suffice for score keeping but not for improvement. The improvement wagon has inherent friction. It requires frequent pushes, which are provided partly by measurements. In order to avoid misleading suggestions introduced by random variation, a time series of measurements should be presented as a control chart, especially when the sample size for each period is small. Control charts provide clear means for distinguishing turns in the trail from random bumps and bounces.[4]

Data presentations should be highly visual, because graphic displays engage the reader and communicate rapidly. Tabular displays of numbers are less interesting, more arduous, and often frustrating, to the point that the reader passes on before grasping the point. Clinicians are busy and often impatient with data. Visual presentation is the key to overcoming this barrier. Following sound principles of graphical display augments the power of the data.[5]

Presentation formats should be avoided if they are threatening, embarrassing, or liable to provoke defensiveness. Detachment can be assumed in the audience for research data. It cannot be assumed for measurements collected for improvement, because the target of measurement is the performance of the audience. For this reason, measurements collected in the first instance for score keeping are often not useful for improvement. They carry the risk of provoking more action focused on attacking the data than on improving care. Avoidance of self-defeating formats means emphasizing internal comparisons over time rather than comparisons among service units. It also means avoiding open labeling of service units when comparisons among units are used. It means avoiding open labeling of individual clinicians. Subtler forms of identification must be guarded against as well, for example, identification of service units or individuals through the implications of the sample sizes reported. Failure to attend to these details can be worse than ineffective, because a defensive reaction to presentation of a performance shortfall can stop all improvement activity indefinitely.

Above all, measurement of clinical care for use by clinicians must be motivating. It must demonstrate for the clinician that there is a gap between what he or she wants to happen and what is actually happening. This touchstone provides the best available summary criterion for judging whether proposed measurements should be pursued. The measurement designer should ask the question: Will the results be motivating? And if resources require that some data be collected and other data be left uncollected, the appropriate question is: Which of these data will be most motivating?

And yet, to return to the issue posed at the outset, clinicians often are not motivated by measurements that appear to call for action. They often do not want what they evidently need. Both realism and humility dictate the last and cardinal rule for reporting:

Develop performance reporting by starting with clinicians' goals. There is no substitute for asking clinicians what they want. By asking, measurement designers will discover what is motivating and they will craft a measurement strategy that is likely to result in action for improvement. Data that are requested are likely to acted upon. Data that appear from elsewhere are likely to be attacked.

This is not to say that health care leaders should simply accept clinicians' initial requests as the final measurement plan. Measurement activities are properly subject to iterative assessment and revision in the same way that processes of care are. One task of a physician executive is to lead the process of measurement, revelation of new perceived needs, and redesign of measurement. The appropriate starting place is what physicians and nurses are concerned about. If they are interested in whether their two-year-old patients are immunized, set out to measure what percentage are immunized. This task will lead to defining what counts as being fully immunized, that is, to the construction of a guideline for childhood immunization. Once the baseline rate is measured, questions will arise about why 10-20 percent (typically) of the children are not immunized.

These questions will lead to measurement of care processes, for example, how often opportunities for immunization are missed in the course of children's visits. Depending on the result, health center procedures may be changed—and measurements later repeated.

The cycle of improvement begins of necessity with the goals and concerns of those actually providing health care.[6] It leads to explorations of the systems for providing care and to design, implementation, and measurement of processes. This activity includes health care guideline development, implementation, and measurement.[7] Repeating the cycle of inquiry and action with an accumulating list of clinical topics leads eventually to a cultural change in the organization. Group development of guidelines becomes commonplace. Clinicians develop a hunger for information about clinical care. These changes occur once clinicians become familiar with the connection between process improvement and their patient-centered goals.

Clinicians who manage both patient information and process information are the clinicians of the future. One privilege of a physician executive is to lead this transformation. The four rules summarized in the table below are offered as a guide for the endeavor.

GUIDE FOR REPORTING PERFORMANCE TO CLINICIANS

Report performance for a service unit that the clinician can influence.
- Avoid units that are too large.
- Avoid individual physician reporting for most topics.
- Focus on functional teams or care units.

Report measurements in a manner that permits evaluation.
- Avoid descriptive reporting.
- Emphasize repeated measurements for a given service unit over time.
- Compare actual practice with current best process.

Report performance to empower decision making.
- Aim to measure for improvement, not research or score keeping.
- Report promptly and frequently.
- Present data visually.
- Avoid presentations that threaten or provoke defensiveness.
- Report to motivate.

Start with clinicians' goals.
- Ask clinicians what they want measured.
- Develop performance reporting iteratively.

References

1. Donabedian, A. *Explorations in Quality Assessment and Monitoring, Volume I: The Definition of Quality and Approaches to Its Assessment.* Ann Arbor, Mich.: Health Administration Press, 1980, pp. 3-31.

2. Cochrane, A. *Effectiveness and Efficiency: Random Reflections on Health Services.* London, England: Nuffield Provincial Hospitals Trust, 1972, pp. 1-7.

3. Walton, M. *The Deming Management Method.* New York, N.Y.: Putnam Publishing Group, 1986, pp. 107-9.

4. Wheeler, D. *Understanding Variation: The Key to Managing Chaos.* Knoxville, Tenn.: SPC Press, Inc., 1993.

5. Tufte, E. *The Visual Display of Quantitative Information.* Cheshire, Conn.: Graphics Press, 1983.

6. Berwick, D. "Continuous Improvement as an Ideal in Health Care." *New England Journal of Medicine* 320(1):53-6, Jan. 5, 1989.

7. Gottlieb, L., and others. "Algorithm-Based Clinical Quality Improvement: Clinical Guidelines and Continuous Quality Improvement." *HMO Practice* 6(1):5-12, March 1992.

Acknowledgments

The author thanks Attilio V. Granata, MD, Paul H. LaMarche, MD, Sharon McDonald, RN, PhD, Stephen C. Schoenbaum, MD, and Michael Werdmann, MD, who provided helpful comments on an earlier draft of this chapter.

CHAPTER 9

The Applicability of Modern Quality Methods to Clinical Decision Making

by David Blumenthal, MD, MPP

There is increasing recognition of the pressing need for a new set of tools and techniques that can assist physicians to practice rational, scientifically sound medicine; to learn from their daily work; and to improve continuously their clinical performance and the health of their patients.[1,2] The use of modern quality management methods perfected in the industrial setting—variously known as total quality management (TQM) and continuous quality improvement (CQI)—has constituted an increasingly popular response to this need.[3]

Although the similarities are not always appreciated, total quality management has much in common with what Wennberg has called the "clinical evaluative sciences": outcomes research, clinical epidemiology, and methods of controlled and uncontrolled experimentation.[4] Both TQM and the clinical evaluative sciences aim to assist physicians and health care systems to improve quality of care and service, and both rely heavily on statistical and experimental methods to accomplish this goal. As with outcomes studies, TQM appreciates that variation—including variations in the outcomes of care—is endemic in all health care, and that much can be learned from analyzing the sources of that variation.[5,6] As with clinical epidemiology, TQM relies on proven statistical methods to explore the relationship between variation in the process of care and variation in the outcomes or quality of what is produced. And as in the experimental sciences, TQM teaches that hypotheses about ways to improve quality should be tested through conduct of controlled or uncontrolled experiments, collection of data on experimental results, and reassessment of interventions based on those results.[7] The experimental process is, in fact, at the heart of the well-known "Plan, Do, Check, Act" (PDCA) cycle of TQM (see Chapter 13).[8]

One of the distinctive contributions and characteristics of total quality management is that it has refined the evaluative sciences to make them user-friendly. Through decades of industrial application, TQM has developed simple but scientifically sound techniques for analyzing variation in processes, learning from that variation, and testing and implementing process improvements.[5] This applied technology for quality management has proved useful in many industrial settings.

A large number of health care organizations have begun the process of adapting the tools and techniques of TQM to improving the quality of the products they provide. Yet, recent studies[9,10] have confirmed a widespread impression that physicians have been reluctant to embrace and participate in TQM activities. Given physicians' influence or control over the processes of health care, their cooperation—indeed, their enthusiastic support—is essential to realizing the theoretical and practical promise of modern quality management methods, as embodied in total quality management and the evaluative sciences underlying it.

The reasons for physicians' resistance to total quality management are undoubtedly multiple. Some have been put off by the quasi-religious rhetoric with which TQM is introduced in some settings.[10] Some view it as just another managerial device to control costs.[11] Because of heavy clinical responsibilities, some simply haven't had time to be educated on the uses of modern quality management methods.[10]

However, a more fundamental and important cause of physician resistance may lie in the fact that advocates of this new approach to quality management are only beginning to develop and have not yet perfected a persuasive conceptual or empirical argument that the techniques and activities of TQM can improve the diagnosis and treatment of health care problems in individual patients.[6] The development of such a case is likely to be enormously helpful in winning the support of physicians for the implementation of total quality management in health care organizations. The reason is that individual patient care is work that physicians are trained and conditioned by experience to view as their own. Until TQM can be demonstrated to have relevance to this work, the likelihood persists that physicians will view TQM as alien—someone else's methods, imposed from without. Therefore, making a case for this relevance to patient care is, in our view, a central challenge facing the quality improvement movement generally, and advocates of TQM and the clinical evaluative sciences in particular.

To illustrate this point more directly, consider the following alternative scenarios. The first has been observed repeatedly by the author in health care organizations around the country.[10] The second suggests what might happen if the hypothesis advanced in this proposal proves valid.

Scenario 1: Quality Improvement by Transformation.

The lay president of Hospital X goes to a seminar on total quality management. He is impressed by what he hears— both its scientific aspects and its lessons for changing organizational culture to make quality "job one." He feels that TQM can be used to improve the quality of care and service at his organization and to cut costs.

The president sends all his senior staff, including medical leadership, to the same seminar. They are similarly impressed and Hospital X decides to become a "TQM organization," hires an outside consultant, develops a "roll-out strategy," and undertakes 10 model projects, the results of which are eagerly awaited so that an empirical case for the utility of TQM can be made.

The projects have the following sorts of aims: to reduce waits in the emergency department, to reduce medication errors, to reduce the time it takes to prepare an operating room for the next procedure, and to cut length of stay for patients undergoing total hip replacement. Interdisciplinary teams are put together to address each of these problems. They include physicians and nonphysicians, all of whom receive "just-in-time" training in TQM. This involves just enough instruction so that they can participate in the problem-solving exercise. The training materials contain illustrative cases similar to those that the hospital is undertaking.

After a year, five of the projects are successful, three are promising but incomplete, and two have failed to show any results and have been abandoned. Senior managers feel that this is an exemplary record and want to greatly expand the TQM strategy, to send all physicians for training, to use TQM to improve quality of patient care in major diagnostic groups in the hospital, etc. They are surprised to find that most physicians (with the exception of a handful of "converts") are unwilling to take three days away from their offices for training, don't show up for the 40 new teams that are started, criticize the data showing the success of past projects, and question the validity of statistics they are presented on their own clinical performance. They are further startled to find that most physicians in their organization have no idea what total quality management involves; are not interested in learning; and confide that, if management would just fix the medical records department, the laboratory, and the scheduling system (using whatever techniques they care to) and would leave the doctors alone to take care of their patients, the hospital would do just fine.

Confused and frustrated, the president decides to avoid clinical issues altogether and pushes forward (at a reduced pace) to improve administrative and financial processes, hoping at some point in the future to apply TQM to the actual care of patients. Secretly, the president is disappointed and angry with his medical staff and decides that most of the profession is profoundly short-sighted, insular, and resistant to change.

Scenario 2: Advanced Patient Care Management.

This scenario starts just as the preceding one did. However, when medical leadership comes back from the outside seminar on TQM, the president is startled to find that they are already familiar with many of the techniques embodied in TQM. He is further startled to learn that physician leaders believe they and their colleagues use very similar techniques in their daily care of patients. This contention is confirmed when physicians who participate in the 10 pilot projects launched by Hospital X prove knowledgeable about many of TQM's core quality improvement approaches and actually become instructors for the nonphysician members of the pilot teams. Physicians believe it makes eminent sense to apply the same tools to improving administrative processes and express the view that they always wondered why management hadn't done so before. After all, what managers call TQM is nothing but sound, scientific, data-based decision making.

How, the president asks his medical leaders, did physicians become so knowledgeable about TQM? The answer, he is told, is that all physicians in medical school now take a course known as "Advanced Techniques for Patient Care Management." The course covers much the same content as the TQM seminar (although, admittedly, it was never called TQM, and there was no discussion about cultural change and organizational transformation). It used very concrete clinical cases that demonstrated how "TQM" could improve clinical decision making and outcomes for common diagnostic problems (such as diabetes, hypertension, asthma, anticoagulation, home dialysis, ventilator management, monitoring of antibiotic levels in septic patients, and total parenteral nutrition) encountered in a variety of clinical settings, including ambulatory practice, the intensive care unit, and management of chronic illness in the home.

Rationale for the Clinical Utility of TQM

The rosy second scenario is predicated on the central and unproven hypothesis that the techniques of total quality management can, in fact, be used to improve the care of individual patients by individual physicians. The rationale for advancing this hypothesis starts with the insight that important similarities may exist between the work of improving quality in complex industrial organizations and the work of patient management in daily medical practice. These similarities become clear—and may be most readily understandable to physicians—by drawing out the similarities between the industrial processes that TQM was created to manage and the biological processes that physicians superintend for their patients.

As every medical student appreciates, physicians are trained to think about patients and their problems using certain models. Prominent among these are models that portray physiologic processes that have clinical relevance, for example, the processes that regulate blood pressure, temperature, heart rate, the clotting of blood, or the synthesis of cholesterol. Medical students learn that the body regulates its vital functions by regulating these biological processes and monitors the results constantly to make necessary adjustments. In these processes, biological inputs, such as chemical transmitters, enzymes, or energy-containing molecules, undergo biological modification (often in a sequence of steps mediated by biochemical, electrical, or physical processes) to produce the outputs the body depends on: the transmission of a chemical signal, the development of a substrate for another reaction, the release of necessary energy, the passage of an electrical signal. When discussing these mechanisms, medical textbooks and professors often use flowcharts with inputs, boxes, arrows, and outputs that closely resemble the flowcharts used by TQM to describe industrial processes. Many biological processes, with slightly different labels, would look indistinguishable on paper from many of the mechanisms that govern the functioning of large companies.

To extend the analogy, one can view the processes of human physiology as being "in control" or "out of control," just as an industrial process might be. Most of the time, in both health and disease, physiologic processes are continuously and tightly controlled. One challenge facing physicians, as it does the controllers who monitor industrial functions, is to measure, interpret, and react appropriately to variations in these processes to understand whether they remain stable and in control or whether they have become unstable and are out of control. Disease may result from loss of stability, stability at an abnormal level, or both (blood pressure may be too variable, stable at too low a level, or both unstable and too low).

Diagnosing instability in a process and distinguishing normal from clinically significant variation are precisely the types of problems that many of the techniques used in total quality management were designed to address. A set of tools known as "statistical process control" (SPC) were developed for this purpose early in the 20th Century and have been perfected for industrial use over the past 80 years.[7] One very useful device, the control chart, has been applied in industry for decades to monitor and interpret variability in industrial processes.[5] Recently, computer software has been developed that can capture data from biological processes (for example, temperature, heart rate, or respiratory rate) and display them in control charts in real time.[12]

An example of a control chart appears in the figure below. It h
the prothrombin ratio of an anticoagulated patient with an ar*
observed ratio of the patient's prothrombin time to the standar*
onds. The upper and lower control limits represent two stanc*
mean of the patient's observed prothrombin ratio over the p*
control chart displays the patient's laboratory data in a readily consu.
allows rapid and statistically sound appraisal of whether the desired level of hemu...
has been reached (mean prothrombin ratio) and of the stability of that level (apparent
both in the control limits and in the variability of observed prothrombin ratios over
time).

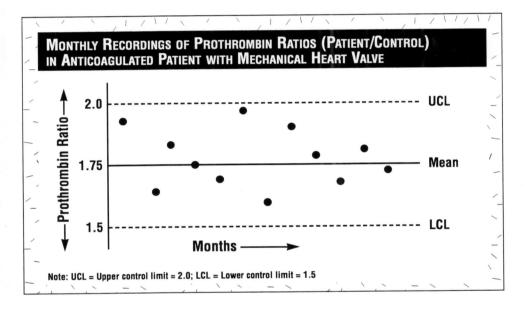

The analogy between biological and industrial processes does not need to be exact to
be useful. The real question is: Are there enough similarities to permit industrial quality management techniques to be applied in a helpful manner to the care of patients in
daily practice? In this regard, there are some very intriguing preliminary indicators.

First, an increasing number of published reports document successful application of
techniques of total quality management to the improvement of clinical care processes.
These examples include reductions in rates of postoperative wound infections,[13] reduction of the use of unnecessary venous catheters in patients on inpatient medical services,[14] and reductions in time to pathological diagnosis (sleepless nights) among
women presenting with breast lumps.[10]

Second, the application of insights from statistical process control raises some very
interesting questions that have received insufficient attention in clinical research and
clinical practice. For the most part, these questions concern variability in biological
processes and the importance of such variability for states of health and disease. How

t, for example, is the level of variability in the key markers that physicians fol- such common primary care problems as high blood pressure (blood pressure), diabetes (blood sugar), or asthma (breathing function)? If variability *per se* is portant, what aspect of variability should be followed most closely, and what levels of variability are acceptable in routine clinical care? It has already been demonstrated that variability in prothrombin time, the indicator that physicians follow in patients whose blood is being thinned with anticoagulants, is an independent predictor of complications of this treatment.[15] Variability in heart rate is an independent predictor of mortality in patients who have recently suffered myocardial infarctions.[16] Blood sugar control is increasingly recognized as essential to preventing the long-term complications of diabetes, although the importance of variability (as opposed to average blood sugar) has not been sufficiently studied to date.

Third, if "control" of biological processes is, indeed, important to maintaining health and preventing the deleterious effects of illness, and if the application of SPC can be harnessed to accomplishing this end in routine clinical care, a larger set of questions emerges. To what extent can "control theory," a well-developed branch of mechanical engineering, be usefully applied to thinking about the common clinical issues that physicians confront? Control theory underlies the development of "expert systems" that are responsible for interpreting complex streams of data in real time and using those data to make constant corrections in the way a system operates. Applications include the guidance systems that get satellites to Jupiter, land our commercial airlines and space shuttles, direct robots on assembly lines, and control prosthetic limbs using impulses from a patient's nervous systems and muscles. It is possible to imagine the development of comparable expert systems for the guidance of routine clinical problems in an array of settings: the operating room; the intensive care unit; and, most intriguingly, the management of primary care problems in the home.

An example might be the development of expert systems to control insulin dosage in diabetes. Many diabetics now measure their blood sugars four times a day at home using glucometers. They and their physicians then use those determinations so that patients may adjust their own insulin levels. However, the decision rules used to guide changes in insulin are inexact at best—the result of trial and error. Through the incorporation of statistical process control techniques into expert systems, such adjustments could be made much more reliable and scientific. It is possible to imagine, for example, that, by building in a small computer, glucometers could store information on past blood sugar and insulin levels, create control charts, interpret the significance of changes in those blood sugar levels, and recommend insulin adjustments that reflect months or years of past experience with patients' blood sugars and insulin doses.

"Expert systems," however, need not be so high tech. The "control chart"—used throughout the world by minimally educated workers in thousands of industrial concerns—represents an expert system of sorts. Control charts require nothing more than a pencil, a sheet of paper, and enough education to enter numbers on a graph. Headrick and Neuhauser[17] have demonstrated that patients with hypertension can chart their blood pressures over time on control charts and develop what they call a "mental model" of how their blood pressures vary in response to their medications, stress, and time of day. Using the control chart in pilot studies, patients have been able to figure

Measuring Clinical Care: A Guide for Physician Executives

out which medications worked and which didn't and which types of situations they should avoid in order to keep their blood pressures "under control."

In fact, the application of TQM to clinical care may have its greatest impact through empowering patients rather than doctors. One of the central goals of TQM in industry has been to tap the creativity of workers at all levels of a production process and to engage those employees in improving the process of production. The major approach used by TQM, as previously noted, has been to "democratize" the use of statistics through the development of user-friendly techniques for applying statistical methods to daily work.

The same general strategy makes even greater sense in clinical medicine. Involving patients in their care has been a long-standing goal of enlightened practice and offers enormous potential benefits, especially in situations where "tight control" and early intervention are important to improve the quality and reduce the cost of care. A number of common outpatient situations fit this description, including several of those mentioned above: diabetes, asthma/chronic obstructive pulmonary disease, anticoagulation, total parenteral nutrition in the home, home use of intravenous antibiotics, and management of chronic congestive heart failure, to name a few. By giving patients a simple technology for monitoring the functioning of the physiologic and pathophysiologic processes underlying these abnormal conditions, the professional provider may be able to make patients partners in their care to an extent that has been almost unthinkable in the past. Patients could reliably diagnose exacerbations in their illnesses long before they became serious. They could consult physicians early or adjust medications themselves using preestablished guidelines. The importance of statistical process control in this new arrangement is that it allows patients (and providers) to make statistically sound judgments about the significance of continuously recorded data in real time. Thus, the ability of the patient to make appropriate decisions based on self-monitoring in the home is no longer in question.

Next Steps

The case for the application of techniques of TQM to individual patient management must ultimately be made in the terms that the best physicians will find persuasive: through valid experiments that demonstrate improvements in patient outcomes when the concepts of TQM are applied. Such experiments should begin with pilot studies in a variety of clinical settings. Among the most promising are intensive care units. In ICUs, caretakers continuously monitor many of their patients' physiologic processes: heart rate, respiratory rate, temperature, and blood pressure. This results in a data-rich environment that creates both problems and opportunities. The problems arise from the need to interpret and to draw statistically valid conclusions from a complex stream of data over time. The opportunity stems from the fact that, in many cases, these data are collected by monitors that are themselves computers that can potentially be programmed to transpose this information into control charts in real time.

A number of outpatient conditions also create opportunities for the application of statistical process control to daily patient management. As a practical matter, chronic illnesses in which patients can play a role in monitoring physiologic indicators of control constitute the most promising outpatient situations. These include asthma (home spirometry), diabetes (glucometers), hypertension (ambulatory blood pressure monitoring), and anticoagulation (home monitoring of prothrombin times). Here again, of course, pilot studies demonstrating the feasibility and value of applying statistical process control to these problems are essential. Such studies should probably begin with patients whose conditions have been difficult for physicians to control with the usual approaches.

It is essential as well that medical education—both graduate and undergraduate—devote more time to instruction in the clinical evaluative sciences. Some of this occurs already. Medical schools do offer some of the basic evaluative sciences—exposure to biostatistics, a smattering of epidemiology, and attention to measurement of outcomes. However, this instruction is scattered and superficial and does not include the all-important element of teaching doctors-in-training how to use the evaluative sciences in their daily work. Preclinical training should include instruction in the scientific method generally and in the use of quick, simple methods of data display and analysis that are comparable to those taught in the context of total quality management. Postgraduate medical education should require that residents be exposed to the practical application of these tools and techniques. Faculty willing and able to model the use of such data-based decision making should be rewarded with promotions and support.

The history of quality management science has been described by Wadsworth *et al.*[7] More than 70 years ago, industrial quality management left behind the relatively primitive techniques used by craftsmen and artisans, which relied chiefly on inspecting the product and discarding those with defects, and adopted the techniques of statistical process control. In the immediate post-World War II period, industrial concerns in Japan began adopting the techniques of total quality management. The techniques moved to the United States in the early 1980s. In health care, we are just now considering the potential of statistical process control to assist in our basic work: the monitoring and managing of patient care problems. It is time to begin tapping the vast experience of other sectors with quality improvement technology to be sure that we are taking advantage of all useful methods for improving patient care.

References

1. Greenfield, S., and Nelson, E. "Recent Developments and Future Issues in the Use of Health Status Assessment Measures in Clinical Settings." *Medical Care* 30(5, Suppl.):MS23-41, May 1992.

2. Palmer, R., and Adams, M. "Quality Improvement/Quality Assurance: A Framework in Putting Research to Work in Quality Improvement and Quality Assurance." AHCPR (90-0034), 1993.

3. Grayson, M. "Benchmark TQM Survey Tracks: A New Management Era in Administration." *Hospitals* 66(11):26-7, June 5, 1992.

4. John E. Wennberg, MD, MPH, Professor of Epidemiology, Peggy Y. Thomson Professor for the Evaluative Clinical Sciences, and Director, Center for the Evaluative Clinical Sciences, Dartmouth Medical School, Hanover, N.H., personal communication.

5. Berwick, D. "Controlling Variation in Health Care: A Consultation from Walter Shewart." *Medical Care* 29(12):1212-25, Dec. 1991.

6. Blumenthal, D. "Total Quality Management and Physicians' Clinical Decisions." *JAMA* 269(21):2775-8, June 2, 1993.

7. Wadsworth, H., and others. *Modern Methods for Quality Control and Improvement*. New York, N.Y.: John Wiley & Sons, Inc., 1986.

8. Scherkenbach, W. *The Deming Route*. Washington, D.C: Continuing Engineering Education Press Books, George Washington University, 1986

9. Shortell, S. "Physician Involvement in Quality Improvement: Issues, Challenges and Recommendations." In *Improving Clinical Practice: Total Quality Management and the Physician*, Blumenthal, D., and Scheck, A., Eds. San Francisco, Calif.: Jossey-Bass Publishers, 1995.

10. Blumenthal, D., and Edwards, J. "Involving Physicians in Total Quality Management: Results of a Study." In *Improving Clinical Practice: Total Quality Management and the Physician*, Blumenthal, D., and Scheck, A., Eds. San Francisco, Calif.: Jossey-Bass Publishers, 1995.

11. Greenfield, S. "Continuous Quality Improvement and the Physician: Building Bridges with Outcomes Research." In *Improving Clinical Practice: Total Quality Management and the Physician*, Blumenthal, D., and Scheck, A., Eds. San Francisco, Calif.: Jossey-Bass Publishers, 1995.

12. Richard Zimmerman, Biomedical Quality Control, Inc., Mobile, Ala., personal communication.

13. Classen, D., and others. "The Timing of Prophylactic Administration of Antibiotics and the Risk of Surgical Wound Infection." *New England Journal of Medicine* 326(5):281-6, Jan. 30, 1992

14. Parenti, C., and others. "Reduction of Unnecessary Intravenous Catheter Use. Internal Medicine Staff Participate in Successful Quality Improvement Project." *Archives of Internal Medicine* 154(16):1829-32, Aug. 22, 1994.

15. Fihn, S., and others. "Risk Factors for Complications of Chronic Anticoagulation." *Annals of Internal Medicine* 118(7):511-20, April 1, 1993.

16. van Ravenswaaij-Arts, C., and others. "Heart Rate Variability." *Annals of Internal Medicine*. 118(6):436-47, March 15, 1993.

17. Neuhauser, D. "Applying Statistical Methods of continuous Quality Improvement to Primary Care: Hypertension." In *Improving Clinical Practice: Total Quality Management and the Physician*, Blumenthal, D., and Scheck, A., Eds. San Francisco, Calif.: Jossey-Bass Publishers, 1995.

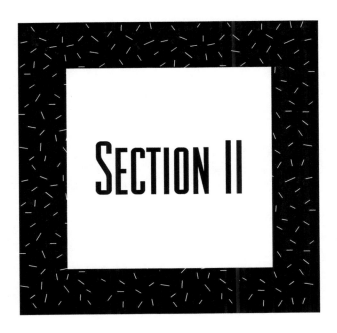

SECTION II

Technical Considerations
in Measurement
of Clinical Care

CHAPTER 10

An Introduction to Risk Adjustment

by Lisa I. Iezzoni, MD, MSc

Before evaluating outcomes of care, it is almost always necessary to consider patient risk. Broadly defined, the goal of risk adjustment is to control for factors that patients independently bring to health care encounters and that can affect their likelihood of experiencing good or bad outcomes. Risk adjustment is generally essential regardless of the outcome under examination (e.g., costs of care, mortality, patient functioning, satisfaction).

Especially when comparing outcomes among providers, risk adjustment "levels the playing field," facilitating comparisons of "apples with apples." Risk adjustment enhances the apparent validity of these comparisons, especially in the eyes of the providers under scrutiny. Without risk adjustment, providers demonstrating poor outcomes have a legitimate concern, reflected by the oft-echoed sentiment, "But my patients are sicker...." To motivate providers on the basis of their outcomes (e.g., to change their clinical practices), it is essential that the information be clinically credible—at a minimum, that it be adjusted for risk.

This chapter introduces the concept of risk adjustment, describes briefly key methodological issues, and suggests what should be considered in choosing a risk-adjustment method. This chapter serves only as an introduction to the field. References are available that provide additional detail, especially about severity-of-illness measures.[1-15]

Conceptual Overview

Unfortunately, consensus typically ends with general agreement about the need for risk adjustment. In many situations, there is no single, correct answer to two major questions:

- What, *exactly*, is meant by "risk?"

- How, *exactly*, should "risk" be measured and quantified?

The general notion of "risk adjustment" eludes a single meaning, because it is inextricably tied to the question: Risk of what? This query can generate myriad responses, ranging from resource consumption to imminent death to complications of care to long-term functional abilities to patient satisfaction. *No single risk-adjustment approach is equally meaningful for all these different outcomes.*

Clinicians have long used words such as "risk," implicitly assuming that their colleagues shared common definitions. In the 1980s, however, many nonclinicians in the health services sector also adopted these terms, prompted primarily by Medicare's move to prospective hospital payment based on diagnosis-related groups (DRGs). "Risk" thus joins other poorly defined but oft-used words and phrases, including "case mix," "severity," "intensity," "complexity," "comorbidity," and "health status." What is clear is that different health care players—clinicians, researchers, administrators, payers, policymakers, financial analysts, quality assessors, regulators, and managers of health care delivery systems—often mean different things when they talk about "risk."

Although a seemingly arcane pursuit, risk-adjustment methods have assumed central importance in recent health management and policy debates at all levels, especially in discussions about monitoring quality of care and deciding how to pay providers.[15-17] To date, much of this discourse has emphasized one major dimension of risk—severity of illness—and has focused on outcomes of acute care hospitalizations.[16,17] Numerous severity measures are now available; a selection of such measures is shown in the table on page 85. Despite the availability of these measures, no definition of severity of illness is uniformly accepted. As Gertman and Lowenstein observed, "'Severity' is what sociologists term a `folk wisdom' word like `satisfaction' or `happiness,' operationally indefinable in a way that is perfectly acceptable to all parties."[25] However, the appropriate applications and potential utility of a severity-of-illness measure derive from how it defines "severity."[1]

As suggested above, the definition of severity depends on who is asked. In many ways, this lack of consensus reflects the realities and uncertainties of current medical practice and knowledge. Even physicians from various specialties have inherently different approaches toward defining severe illness, some related to fundamental variations in delineating the relevant "episode of illness." For instance, intensive care unit and trauma specialists often focus on risk of death within hours or days. Oncologists examine two-, three-, or five-year survival in determining clinical staging criteria for cancer patients. Primary care physicians can look at blood pressure or serum cholesterol levels to anticipate long-term survival, measured in many years or decades. Psychiatrists concentrate on cognitive performance and mental functioning, while physiatrists focus on physical impairment and disability. Neonatologists and pediatricians encompass the breadth of severity perspectives, but the clinical variables that indicate severe illness in infants and children can differ from those observed in adults. Nurses consider both the physiologic perspective of physicians and patients' psychological and dependency attributes. Health care managers emphasize resource needs, implicitly correlating higher severity with higher "intensity" or costs.

In the current environment, one of the most important distinctions is between risk-adjustment approaches focused on clinical outcomes and those addressing cost. Physiological severity and financial burden are not always directly related: Higher severity from a clinical perspective does not invariably lead to greater resource consumption. For example, very ill patients may be treated parsimoniously for several reasons.[26] Patients with severe physiological or biochemical derangements often present significant surgical or procedural

Measuring Clinical Care: A Guide for Physician Executives

EXAMPLES OF SEVERITY MEASURES, THEIR DEFINITIONS OF SEVERITY, AND THEIR DATA REQUIREMENTS

System	Definition of Severity	Data Required
Acuity Index Method (AIM)[11]	Length of hospital stay within DRGs	Administrative data*
All Patient Refined DRGs (APR-DRGs)	Resource consumption within adjacent DRGs†	Administrative data
Acute Physiology and Chronic Health Evaluation (APACHE)[18]	In-hospital mortality for intensive care unit patients	Clinical data
Computerized Severity Index (CSI)[19]	Treatment difficulty presented to physicians on basis of combination of patients' diagnoses and the level of derangement of disease-specific signs and symptoms	Clinical data
Disease Staging Scales	Definition depends on individual scale: total charges/ costs, length of stay, readmission, in-hospital mortality, and complications of care	Administrative data
Disease Staging Stages[20]	Complexity, etiology, and extent of organ system involvement	Administrative or clinical data
MedisGroups[21]	In-hospital mortality	Clinical data
Patient Management Categories (PMCs) Relative Intensity Score[22]	Relative intensity of resources	Administrative data
Pediatric Risk of Mortality Score (PRISM)[23]	In-hospital mortality for children in pediatric intensive care units	Clinical data
Yale University Refined DRGs[24]	Relative hospitalization charges within adjacent DRGs	Administrative data

* Administrative data = standard hospital discharge abstracts, such as computerized UB-82 or UB-92 data.
† Adjacent DRGs are DRGs previously split by patient age or the presence of complications or comorbidities (CCs).

risks and are therefore treated with less expensive, more conservative approaches. Severely affected patients may be easier to diagnose, requiring fewer expensive tests. Terminally ill patients, such as individuals with widely metastatic cancer, may decline to be resuscitated or treated in expensive intensive care units, thus lowering their potential costs.

Because of differing definitions of risk, it is crucial to answer the following question before considering a specific risk-adjustment strategy: what is my purpose? In the health policy arena, information on risk is typically used for one of two primary purposes:

■ To predict resource consumption (e.g., to improve fairness of reimbursement for individual hospitalizations, for an annual fee to capitated insurance plans).

■ To compare and monitor clinical outcomes of care in widespread quality assessment.

These two purposes are typically debated separately, and few have suggested using the same risk-adjustment approach for provider reimbursement and for monitoring more clinical outcomes of care (e.g., mortality rates). For example, although the Health Care Financing Administration (HCFA) bases Medicare's hospital reimbursement upon DRGs, it does not use DRGs for risk adjustment in its annual release of hospital mortality rates. This is appropriate: DRGs were designed to predict resource consumption, not imminent death,[27] while the mortality prediction models are empirically derived specifically to predict deaths.[28] However, comparisons of aggregate costs or charges across hospitals or providers often employ DRGs or scores derived from DRGs, such as the case mix index.[29] A single risk-adjustment approach is not likely to suit all purposes.

Major Methodological Considerations

Designing a risk-adjustment strategy is a complicated exercise. At a minimum, it requires designating risk factors—clinical or other characteristics that reflect patients' likelihood of experiencing the outcome of interest. Once delineated, these risk factors must be "operationalized." For example, they must be defined to permit reliable and unbiased identification and measurement (e.g., whether temperature values should be based on oral or rectal readings; how abstractors should interpret words such as "probable" and "possible"). These risk factors must then be combined in either an empirical or normative fashion to produce a risk score or rating for each patient (e.g., APACHE II adds weights assigned to 12 physiologic parameters, plus age points and chronic health points, to produce its overall score). Several key methodological issues are discussed briefly below.

Role of Diagnosis

A hotly contested debate has been whether risk is a diagnosis-specific construct. Measures can either differ by diagnosis or be independent of diagnosis ("generic"). In a diagnosis-dependent approach, for example, a temperature of 101° fahrenheit may mean something different in a neutropenic cancer patient than in an otherwise healthy patient with acute bronchitis. Generic systems offer the potential benefit of greater simplicity, both in data collection and in arraying data for analysis, but perhaps with an important trade-off in clinical credibility and statistical validity.

Research evidence suggests that the ability of admission clinical findings (e.g., vital signs, serum chemistry results) to predict inpatient survival varies by condition.[30-32]

Despite these practical and analytic considerations, concerns about the role of diagnosis reflect a more fundamental question: *Is the risk-adjustment measure medically meaningful (i.e., clinically valid)?* In other words, is its conceptual formulation consistent with the way that providers form expectations about a patient's clinical course? Medical meaningfulness is not an absolute construct; it must be assessed within the environment in which the information will be employed, by those who will be affected by its use. If the ultimate goal of the information is to change provider behavior (e.g., as in hospital quality assurance), it is crucial that providers agree *a priori* that the approach is actually capturing important risk factors. Otherwise, providers unhappy with their risk-adjusted performance rating may plead a variation of the typical defense: "My patients *are* sicker, but you have not measured risk properly."

Role of Major Surgery and Other Procedures

Another thorny issue involves whether the measure of risk should be independent of everything that happened after the patient began the pertinent health care encounter: *Should the risk adjustment include anything occurring after patient admission?* The answer to this question may depend on one's purpose. For example, some measures (e.g., DRGs, PMCs) define case types by whether major surgery was performed and, if so, by the type of procedure. If the goal is to predict hospitalization costs, including major surgery as a classification variable is important. Most of the explanatory power achieved by the DRGs in predicting costs derives from their ability to group surgical cases with similar, relatively high costs and to differentiate expensive surgical cases from generally cheaper medical cases.[33] For instance, DRGs separate patients admitted for acute myocardial infarction into different groups by whether they received coronary artery bypass surgery (DRGs 106 and 107), percutaneous transluminal coronary angioplasty (DRG 112), or medical treatment (DRGs 121, 122, and 123). In this context, it is important to note that this classification approach *per se* does not provide insight about the appropriateness of major surgery or other procedures, an integral component of quality measurement.[34]

In contrast, if one's goal is to examine risk-adjusted outcomes as an indicator of the quality of care, including information arising after the health care encounter starts may present a problem. Findings from after admission may reflect substandard care—the very quantity of interest. For example, surgery may have been performed because of a failure to diagnose and treat a condition in an appropriate and timely fashion. A wildly deranged laboratory finding may reflect lack of appropriate monitoring and response to mild abnormalities. To address this concern, some of the measures based on clinical data constrain the time window for the severity evaluation. For example, the CSI admission severity rating is based on findings from only the first 6 hours for intensive care unit patients and from the first 24 hours for all others.

A related issue is whether a particular technology should be used to identify risk factors, especially sophisticated diagnostic tests. For example, some MedisGroups key clinical findings (KCFs) derive from coronary angiography, computed tomography scans, and endoscopy. Such findings may be critically important, but using this information could potentially bias comparisons across providers, especially if different hospitals have different technological capabilities or practice patterns. Identical patients could receive different risk assessments depending on the availability and use of a specific diagnostic test; practice patterns could thus confound comparisons of risk-adjusted outcomes. Even using routine laboratory test results could present difficulties in certain situations. For example, if terminally ill patients have requested "comfort measures only" (i.e., refused routine phlebotomy), even minimal laboratory values, such as serum chemistries, will not be available to indicate the level of patient risk. This could result in the paradoxical finding of high mortality among patients with ostensibly "low" severity.

Data Requirements

From a practical perspective, the most important attribute of a risk-adjustment approach involves its data requirements. As shown in the table on page 85, risk-adjustment approaches typically use either computerized discharge abstract data that hospitals already produce to assign the DRGs ("secondary data-based systems"), or they require additional clinical variables abstracted from the medical record or some other primary source ("primary data-based systems"). Those relying exclusively on secondary data are indisputably cheaper to use; however, they may not offer the clinical credibility of a system derived from primary clinical data.

"Secondary" or "administrative" data are generally created by providers (e.g., hospitals, physicians) for billing or other payment-related purposes, such as hospital rate setting. The most common form of these data is the hospital discharge abstract and billing records, such as the Uniform Billing Form (UB-82, UB-92) required by Medicare.[35] These sources contain limited clinical information, including patient age, sex, discharge status (alive/dead), admission type (urgent versus elective), and a limited number of diagnosis and procedure codes (based on the *International Classification of Diseases, Ninth Revision, Clinical Modification,* or ICD-9-CM36).

Given that these records are generally derived from billing activities, they are typically viewed with suspicion by those worried about potential financial motivations underlying data reporting. There are numerous concerns about the clinical content, completeness, and accuracy of ICD-9-CM codes.[37-41] In addition, discharge abstracts generally do not differentiate conditions present on admission from those occurring later in the hospital stay. Therefore, it is impossible to derive an accurate picture of patients' clinical status *on admission* from discharge abstracts alone. Nevertheless, these data have the significant virtue of being readily available and typically all-inclusive (e.g., discharge abstract data are often available across entire populations, offering the potential of comparisons across all providers). They have been a common first step in examining risk-adjusted outcomes information.

Primary or clinical data present their own opportunities and problems. With medical record reviews, one can collect detailed clinical measures that might enhance the medical meaningfulness of the risk-adjustment approach. It is also generally possible to distinguish conditions present on admission from those arising later. However, clinical findings from physical examinations, routine diagnostic testing (e.g., chest x-rays), and even technologically sophisticated studies (e.g., CT scans) are often fraught with vagaries and wide interobserver variations. As Eddy observed, "Uncertainty creeps into

Measuring Clinical Care: A Guide for Physician Executives

medical practice through every pore....And the ambiguities grow worse as medical technology expands."[42] Another concern involves the completeness, accuracy, and validity of information contained in medical records.[43-48] The medical record is increasingly used as a vehicle for cost containment (e.g., through utilization review) and for legal and administrative purposes. This may affect documentation of potentially sensitive clinical concerns, such as psychological disorders, cognitive dysfunctions, substance abuse, and risky sexual practices. In addition, language may be modulated to meet the expectations of the many individuals who can now be expected to have access to the medical record (e.g., utilization reviewers, "peer" reviewers, billing offices, lawyers, patients).[48] Therefore, medical records may not reflect complete and objective accounts of patients' clinical presentations or outcomes.

Reliability

Reliability relates to whether different reviewers scoring the same case produce similar assessment of patient risk. An unreliable measure yields data of suspect quality, thus compromising its utility. The reliability of systems based on discharge abstracts depends on the reliability of diagnostic and procedural coding. Hospital coding practices are often not under the control of the person or group performing the risk assessment, raising inevitable concerns about the financial motivations mentioned above. The reliability of primary data collection derives from various considerations, including the clarity and definition of the requested data elements; the rules established for interpreting terminology and jargon in medical records; the extent to which reviewers must make subjective judgments; the scope of the review (e.g., focusing exclusively on physician notations versus reviewing notes of all caregivers); and the legibility, completeness, timeliness, and organization of the medical records. If reviews are particularly detailed, inter-rater reliability will certainly be affected by basic human considerations, such as morale, motivation, training, supervision, ésprit de corps with fellow reviewers (e.g., extent to which they discuss questions among themselves), and even the environment in which the reviews occur (e.g., lighting, ventilation).

The term "reliability" technically refers to the potential for "random" errors. High random error rates would compromise the utility of the information about risk, but, despite this, the "randomness" of the errors should diffuse their potential impact (i.e., the effect of errors should average out over patients and providers). The true threat to the integrity of risk assessment is the opportunity for nonrandom error and, most important, the possibility of manipulation. Regardless of the risk-adjustment approach, it is likely that its underlying data could be manipulated or "gamed." To minimize the chance of manipulation, the risk-adjusted outcomes data must be perceived as being used in a fair and nonpunitive manner—or at least as providing "due process" for those contesting any findings.

Statistical Performance

Once a risk-adjustment method is developed, it needs to be tested to see how well it actually predicts the outcome of interest from a statistical perspective (e.g., measures of discrimination and calibration). Within the research and health policy communities, much energy has been expended on measuring and attempting to maximize statistical performance (as represented by such statistics as R-squared levels, chi-square values, or areas under receiver-operating characteristics curves).[14] Despite this, relatively little information is available comparing statistical performance across severity measures.[11]

Without entering into a detailed discussion of statistical considerations it is important to note that it is unlikely that any risk-adjustment system will perfectly predict outcomes. In today's environment, which is so enamored of "facts" and statistics, one is tempted to believe that models can be built that will accurately answer all questions—such as predicting which patients will have bad outcomes—and control for all potential confounding variables. This is not possible in most clinical settings: too much uncertainty exists, with the potential for "random events" or "acts of God." Given these limitations, risk-adjustment approaches cannot be expected to provide perfect predictions that could guide individual patient care.

Choosing a Risk Adjustment Approach

As suggested above, a variety of factors should be considered when choosing a risk-adjustment approach. Questions to ask before choosing a risk-adjustment system include:

■ *What is the purpose of the risk adjustment?*

As emphasized earlier, different approaches are required to look at different outcomes. In particular, risk-adjustment methods focused on resource consumption may be quite different from those examining clinical outcomes. It is unlikely that a single risk-adjustment measure will satisfy all needs. In choosing a measure, it is therefore necessary to select one developed for the envisioned use. For example, if one's purpose is to explain hospitalization costs, choosing a risk-adjustment method developed to predict mortality would be inappropriate.

■ *Is the methodology clinically meaningful?*

As suggested above, clinical meaningfulness must be considered within the clinical context—it is not a fixed, immutable quantity. For example, measures developed to predict mortality from coronary artery bypass grafts may be clinically credible for that purpose; they may contain the types of clinical factors shown in clinical trials to affect patient outcomes and to be accepted by clinicians in the field (e.g., whether the left anterior descending coronary artery is involved, the percentage occlusion of this vessel, the cardiac ejection fraction). However, these risk factors are unlikely to be the most pertinent ones for patients undergoing colectomy for bowel cancer.

Clinical credibility is crucial if one hopes to motivate physicians on the basis of information derived from the severity measure. Therefore, it needs to be judged ultimately by the physicians who will be affected by the information. One way of assessing the clinical content of a severity measure, for example, is to have clinicians review a series of their medical records and provide their own normative severity rating of each case. They also can be asked to indicate what clinical factors caused them to rate each case the way they did. Candidate severity measurement systems can be applied to the same records. Then the ratings and pertinent clinical factors provided by the

Measuring Clinical Care: A Guide for Physician Executives

clinicians and by the severity system can be compared. If there is good concordance between the two, it is likely that the physicians will view the severity measure as clinically meaningful. If not, additional consideration may be required to devise an acceptable risk-adjustment approach that will have the credibility essential to motivate physicians.

■ *Does the approach capture unique features of the institutions whose outcomes will be evaluated?*

Risk-adjustment approaches may need to be sensitive to special features of the institutions under study. For example, different approaches may be needed for children's hospitals, rehabilitation or chronic disease facilities, substance abuse and detoxification centers, and psychiatric institutions. Facilities treating many patients on research protocols, such as cancer institutes, may present a situation in which diagnostic testing and routine monitoring are explicitly delineated. Therefore, the information available to evaluate "risk" will be that specified by the protocol. Tertiary teaching facilities have many physicians documenting the medical record, whereas physicians may spend a limited amount of time daily at small, rural hospitals. If a severity measure requires all risk factors to be taken from physician notes, patients at tertiary facilities could appear sicker than those at smaller institutions because of documentation bias. Special attention may be needed to judge hospitals that accept many patients in transfer. For instance, such patients are routinely stabilized prior to transfer, and therefore may not demonstrate profound physiologic derangements at the time of acceptance at the receiving hospital. Such patients may nonetheless be at high risk, despite relatively normal admission findings.

■ *Is the logic available in a way that is easy to understand?*

To be able to judge clinical credibility and the sensitivity of a measure to special features of a patient population, it is essential that the logic of the risk-adjustment system be available. Not only must the logic be available, but also it must be presented in a manner that is transparent and easy to digest. While this seems a fair request, it is important to note that the health care data industry is currently highly competitive, especially as health care reform nears. Many proprietary systems have guarded their logic as a "black box" to protect the financial interests of their vendors.[49] In addition, the "logic" of many empirically derived risk-adjustment systems is, by definition, steeped in statistical constructs that may not be readily obvious to the average clinician. Educating physicians to make them more comfortable with statistical methodologies may be necessary. However, it is also reasonable to request that suppliers of risk-adjustment systems attempt to explain their logic in a clear and meaningful fashion.

■ *What data are required to perform the risk assessment?*

As stated above, data requirements will, to a large extent, determine the cost and feasibility of using a risk-adjustment system. Approaches drawn from existing administrative data are certainly cheaper than those requiring *de novo* data collection, but they entail a potential compromise of clinical credibility. Regardless of which approach is adopted, however, it may be necessary to change the ways in which documentation is performed in the hospital. For example, if administrative data are used, encouraging more complete diagnostic coding may be necessary. If data from medical records are used, the hospital may need to speed the flow of laboratory and test reports to the chart, to improve record documentation and organization, and to ensure the legibility and completeness of all information. "Paperless" medical records (i.e., those in which all documentation is electronically stored and computer-accessible) may ultimately make the job of risk assessment much easier. For example, values from the clinical laboratories could be downloaded directly into a severity measurement algorithm and severity scores automatically computed.

■ *Is the system relatively immune to manipulation?*

It is possible to "game" most risk-adjustment systems, except perhaps those that depend solely on laboratory- or machine-generated measures. However, if one is sufficiently cynical, even these relatively immune values could possibly be manipulated: for example, an arterial blood gas could be drawn with the patient's inspiratory oxygen flow rate temporarily set at a lower level to depress (transiently) the arterial oxygenation value. Despite this possibility, given the strong countervailing ethos of medicine (e.g., the Hippocratic tradition of "first, do no harm"), it is difficult to imagine that physicians would succumb to such Machiavellian motivation to compromise patient care. However, less egregious examples of manipulating the data (e.g., not documenting or overdocumenting certain findings in the medical record) are imaginable. As suggested earlier, the best guard against manipulation is to use the data fairly and in a constructive dialogue with clinicians. If the data are used unfairly in an explicitly punitive fashion, efforts to "game" the system are more likely. If the quality of the data is damaged by gaming, questions about the meaning and objectivity of the risk adjustments are inevitable.

■ *How much will the risk assessment cost?*

Some costs are obvious: e.g., computer software development or software licenses; computer hardware; staff to abstract and enter the data; space to put the staff; and costs necessary to improve documentation. A hidden cost may be increased diagnostic testing ordered by physicians to demonstrate the severity of their patients. Finally, an important cost involves staff highly skilled in analytic methods who can help make sense of the data coming from the risk-assessment system.

Conclusions
Risk adjustment is generally essential to comparing patient outcomes across providers, health care systems, or treatment options. The optimal risk-adjustment approach varies, depending on the outcome of interest (e.g., costs of care versus imminent death) and the resources available to spend on performing the risk adjustment (e.g., collecting severity information). No single risk-adjustment approach is equally suited to every purpose. In addition, it is unlikely that any risk-assessment method will perfectly predict outcomes for individual patients. For example, none of the currently available severity measures controls completely for all patient factors that may relate to poor outcomes

(e.g., socioeconomic status, functional level). Nevertheless, when applied across groups of patients, risk adjustment facilitates interpretation of outcomes information.

References

1. Hornbrook, M. "Hospital Case Mix: Its Definition, Measurement and Use: Part I. The Conceptual Framework." *Medical Care Review* 39(1):1-43, Spring 1982.

2. Hornbrook, M. "Hospital Case Mix: Its Definition, Measurement and Use: Part II. Review of Alternative Measures." *Medical Care Review* 39(2):73-123, Summer 1982.

3. Hornbrook, M. "Techniques for Assessing Hospital Case Mix." *Annual Review of Public Health* 6:295-324, 1985.

4. Cretin, S., and Worthman, L. *Alternative Systems for Case Mix Classification in Health Care Financing.* Santa Monica, Calif.: The Rand Corporation (R-3457-HCFA), 1986.

5. Jencks, S., and Dobson, A. "Refining Case-Mix Adjustment. The Research Evidence." *New England Journal of Medicine* 317(11):679-86, Sept. 10, 1987.

6. McMahon, L., and Billi, J. "Measurement of Severity of Illness and the Medicare Prospective Payment System. State of the Art and Future Directions." *Journal of General Internal Medicine* 3(5):482-90, Sept.-Oct. 1988.

7. Aronow, D. Severity-of-Illness Measurement: Applications in Quality Assurance and Utilization Review." *Medical Care Review* 45(2):339-66, Fall 1988.

8. Geehr, E. *Selecting a Proprietary Severity-of-Illness System.* Tampa, Fla.: American College of Physician Executives, 1989.

9. The Quality Measurement and Management Project. *The Hospital Administrator's Guide to Severity Measurement Systems.* Chicago, Ill.: Hospital Research and Educational Trust of the American Hospital Association, 1989.

10. Thomas, J., and Ashcraft, M. "Measuring Severity of Illness: A Comparison of Interrater Reliability among Severity Methodologies." *Inquiry* 26(4):483-92, Winter 1989.

11. Thomas, J., and Ashcraft, M. "Measuring Severity of Illness: Six Severity Systems and Their Ability to Explain Cost Variations." *Inquiry* 28(1):39-55, Spring 1991.

12. Iezzoni, L. "Severity Standardization and Hospital Quality Assessment." In Couch, J., Ed., *Health Care Quality Management for the 21st Century.* Tampa, Fla.: American College of Physician Executives, 1991, pp. 177-234.

13. Iezzoni, L. "Risk Adjustment for Medical Outcomes Studies." In Grady, M., Ed., *Medical Effectiveness Research Data Methods.* Rockville, Md.: Agency for Health Care Policy and Research, June 1992:83-97. Association for Health Care Policy and Research 92-0056.

14. Iezzoni, L. "Severity of Illness Measures and Assessing the Quality of Hospital Care." In Goldfield, N., and Nash, D., Eds. *Providing Quality Care: The Challenge to Clinicians and Administrators,* Second Edition. Ann Arbor, Mich: Health Administration Press, 1995.

15. Iezzoni, L., Ed. *Risk Adjustment for Measuring Health Care Outcomes.* Ann Arbor, Mich.: Health Administration Press, 1994.

16. Iezzoni, L., and others. "The Role of Severity Iformation in Health Policy Debates: A Survey of State and Regional Concerns." *Inquiry* 28(2):117-28, Summer 1991.

17. Iezzoni, L., and Greenberg, L. "Widespread Assessment of Risk-Adjusted Outcomes: Lessons from Local Initiatives." *Joint Commission Journal on Quality Improvement* 20(6):305-16, June 1994.

18. Knaus, W., and others. "The APACHE III Prognostic System: Risk Prediction of Hospital Mortality for Critically Ill Hospitalized Adults." *Chest* 100(6):1619-36, Dec. 1991.

19. Horn, S., and others. "The Relationship between Severity of Illness and Hospital Length of Stay and Mortality." *Medical Care* 29(4):305-17, April 1991.

20. Gonnella, J., and others. "Staging of Disease: A Case-Mix Measurement." *JAMA* 251(5):637-44, Feb. 3, 1984.

21. Steen, P., and others. "Predicted Probabilities of Hospital Death as a Measure of Admission Severity of Illness." *Inquiry* 30(2):128-41, Summer 1993.

22. Young, W., and others. "The Measurement of Hospital Case Mix." *Medical Care* 20(5):501-12, May 1982.

23. Freeman, J., and others. "Refinement." In Fetter, R., and others, Eds. *DRGs: Their Design and Development.* Ann Arbor, Mich.: Health Administration Press, 199, pp. 57-79.

24. Pollack, M.,and others. "Pediatric Risk of Mortality (PRISM) Score. *Critical Care Medicine* 16(11):1110-6, Nov. 1988.

25. Gertman, P., and Lowenstein, S". A Research Paradigm for Severity of Illness: Issues for the Diagnosis-Related Group System. *Health Care Financing Review* annual suppl:79-90, 1984.

26. Smits, H., and others. "Variation in Resource Use within Diagnosis-Related Groups: The Severity Issue." *Health Care Financing Review* annual suppl:71-8, 1984.

27. Fetter, R., and others. "Case Mix Definition by Diagnosis Related Groups." *Medical Care* 18(2 suppl):1-53, Feb. 1980.

28. Sullivan, L., and Wilensky, G. *Medicare Hospital Mortality Information. 1987, 1988, 1989.* Washington, D.C.: U.S. Department of Health and Human Services, Health Care Financing Administration, 1991.

29. *Report and Recommendations to the Congress, March 1, 1993.* Washington, D.C.: Prospective Payment Assessment Commission, 1993.

30. Keeler, E., and others. "Changes in Sickness at Admission Following the Introduction of the Prospective Payment System." *JAMA* 264(15):1962-8, Oct. 17, 1990.

31. Daley, J., and others. "Predicting Hospital-Associated Mortality for Medicare Patients. A Method for Patients with Stroke, Pneumonia, Acute Myocardial Infarction, and Congestive Heart Failure." *JAMA* 260(24):3617-24, Dec. 23-30, 1988.

32. Iezzoni, L., and others. "Predicting In-Hospital Mortality: A Comparison of Severity Measurement Approaches." *Medical Care* 30(4):347-59, April 1992.

33. Iezzoni, L., and others. "Admission MedisGroups Score and the Cost of Hospitalizations." *Medical Care* 26(11):1068-80, Nov. 1988.

34. Payne, S. "Identifying and Managing Inappropriate Hospital Utilization: A Policy Synthesis." *Health Services Research* 22(5):709-69, Dec. 1987.

35. U.S. Congress, Office of Technology Assessment. *Medicare's Prospective Payment System: Strategies for Evaluating Cost, Quality, and Medical Technology.* Washington, D.C.: U.S. Government Printing Office Publication OTA-H-262, 1985, pp. 195-9.

36. Public Health Service-Health Care Financing Administration, U.S. Department of Health and Human Services. *International Classification of Diseases, Ninth Revision, Clinical Modification. Third Edition.* Washington, D.C.: U.S. Government Printing Office, 1989.

37. Hsia, D., and others. "Accuracy of Diagnostic Coding for Medicare Patients under the Prospective-Payment System." *New England Journal of Medicine* 318(6):352-5, Feb. 11, 1988.

38. Hsia, D., and others. "Medicare Reimbursement Accuracy under the Prospective Payment System, 1985 to 1988." *JAMA* 268(7):896-9, Aug. 19, 1992.

39. McMahon, L., and Smits, H. "Can Medicare Prospective Payment Survive the ICD-9-CM Disease Classification System?" *Annals of Internal Medicine* 104(4):562-6, April 1986.

40. Fisher, E., and others. "The Accuracy of Medicare's Hospital Claims Data: Progress Has Been Made, but Problems Remain." *American Journal of Public Health* 82(2):243-8, Feb. 1992.

41. Iezzoni, L., and others. "Comorbidities, Complications, and Coding Bias. Does the Number of Diagnosis Codes Matter in Predicting In-Hospital Mortality?" *JAMA* 267(16):2197-203, April 22-29, 1992.

42. Eddy, D. "Variations in Physician Practice: The Role of Uncertainty." *Health Affairs* 3(2):74-89, Summer 1984.

43. Romm, F., and Putnam, S. "The Validity of the Medical Record." *Medical Care* 19(3):310-5, March 1981.

44. Starfield, B., and others. "Concordance between Medical Records and Observations Regarding Information on Coordination of Care." *Medical Care* 17(7):758-66, July 1979.

45. Feigl, P., and others. "Studying Patterns of Cancer Care: How Useful Is the Medical Record?" *American Journal of Public Health* 78(5):526-33, May 1988.

46. Kosecoff, J., and others. "The Appropriateness of Using a Medical Procedure. Is Information in the Medical Record Valid?" *Medical Care* 25(3):196-201, March 1987.

47. Iezzoni, L., and others. *Diagnostic Mix, Illness Severity, and Cost in Teaching and Nonteaching Hospitals.* Boston, Mass.: Health Care Research Unit, Boston University Medical Center; January 1989. Prepared for the Health Care Financing Administration under Cooperative Agreement No. 15-C-98835/1-02.

48. Burnum, J. "The Misinformation Era: The Fall of the Medical Record." *Annals of Internal Medicine* 110(6):482-4, March 15, 1989.

49. Iezzoni, L. "'Black Box' Medical Information Systems: A Technology Needing Assessment." *JAMA* 265(22):3006-7, June 12, 1991.

CHAPTER 11

Listening to Patients:
Bringing Quality Measurement to Life

by Joseph M. Healy Jr., PhD

Consider the following scenarios, based on the experiences of real patients:

A patient experiencing pain and limited use of his foot visits his internist. After evaluation, the internist refers the patient to orthopedics. The patient is told he will have to wait three weeks for an appointment. The patient waits and suffers with his limitation, figuring the orthopedist will know what to do. On the day of the appointment, the patient waits in the exam room. After a brief wait, a man in a white coat enters and says, "Hi, my name is Alex. I'm not a doctor. I'm a physician's assistant. What can I do for you today?"

A 35-year-old woman wakes up three nights a week with symptoms of asthma. She experiences wheezing and coughing on most days, but figures that it is just part of being asthmatic. She uses a beta agonist when she feels the need and only sees a physician for check-ups and to get her prescription refilled. She typically misses one day a month from work because of her asthma. She likes to jog but is afraid to exercise when her asthma is acting up.

A young man has been experiencing chest pain and describes his recent history, including symptoms, diet, exercise, job stress, and marital difficulties. His internist refers him to a cardiologist. After asking the patient to repeat his story and completing an office-based evaluation, the cardiologist refers the patient to a lab at a nearby hospital for noninvasive testing and schedules a follow up visit. When the man arrives at the hospital, the lab staff do not know who he is or what tests he is supposed to have. The patient is sent home and, after clearing up the confusion, completes the tests at a later visit. When he returns for his follow-up visit with the cardiologist, she does not yet have the test results and is unable to proceed with a treatment plan.

These scenarios are included not because they illustrate problems in delivery of health care, but rather because they identify several different kinds of information not routinely documented in medical records, hospital charts, claims systems, or lab reports. Our window on what happens in health care delivery and its impact on patients is limited to what happens within the walls of our own offices, clinics, labs, and hospitals. As health care providers, we carefully document history; diagnoses; treatment plans; utilization of various services; test results; and, to a lesser extent, outcomes.

The quality measures that come from these records (e.g., mammography rates, time to follow-up of abnormal Pap smears, postoperative infection rates, catheterization rates, and revascularization results) are critical but impersonal components of a quality information system.

Our documentation and records leave out much that is relevant to understanding the quality and outcomes of care. In particular, they do not give us a personal or service perspective on quality. No hospital claim will capture the patient's wasted visit to the lab or the wasted staff time in clearing up the confusion. No encounter form will describe the patient's displeasure with having had to wait three weeks to see an orthopedic physician's assistant, even if the PA provided excellent care. No chart will document the circumstances in which a mild asthmatic chooses to use her inhaler, and only a very thorough history will reveal that she misses 12 work days per year due to asthma. Because each patient is a living database of information about his or her own health and illnesses, health care experience, and its impact on well-being and satisfaction, the patient perspective is an invaluable resource and will add richness to any quality measurement plan.

Why Ask Patients About Quality?
Competitive market pressures, the quality management movement, and purchaser and regulator demands are magnifying the need for hospitals, health plans, clinics, physicians, laboratories, and product manufacturers to report quality information. More important, to improve quality and control costs in health care organizations, we must routinely collect and analyze information about the quality of care and services we provide. Ten years ago, the origin of the patient-based quality measurement movement in health care focused on patient satisfaction. Now we recognize and appreciate that patients can tell us much more about the process of care, their involvement in it, and its impact on them than just how satisfied they are.[1,2]

As health care reform evolves, health care organizations are establishing networks, alliances, and affiliations to provide integrated, coordinated care for their populations. High-quality, cost-effective health care that meets the needs of both populations and individuals will require complex and enriched quality information to monitor and manage the quality of care provided. There will be some lag time before integrated information systems are available to monitor quality in such a complex and decentralized delivery system. Patients' experiences represent an information resource that can be easily accessed to understand the impact of the delivery system on quality and satisfaction.

Purchasers, regulators, product manufacturers, and health care providers are increasingly interested in understanding the impact of illness and health care on the functioning and well-being of patients after they leave the clinic, office, or hospital. We are no longer comfortable assuming that, if patients do not return, they are completely recovered, satisfied, and functioning optimally. In fact, we know all too well that patients live with unnecessary health limitations and burdens. By asking patients, we can understand the impact of illness and health care on their lives. Let us consider, then, what information we might gather from patients and potential patients as part of our quality measurement strategy.

The Patient as the Ideal Source of Information

Clearly, patients are the only ones who can tell us whether they are satisfied or not with the care they receive. We are able to ask patients routinely about their satisfaction with encounters or processes (e.g., office visits, hospitalizations, outpatient procedures, specialty referrals, specific tests) as well as their satisfaction with the care provided for specific health problems (e.g., asthma, labor and delivery, diabetes, urinary incontinence). As the quality movement matures, physicians' and managers' interest in and need for information regarding patient satisfaction has grown. Some organizations are routinely tracking patient satisfaction with key clinical services (e.g., cardiac care, prenatal care, outpatient mental health care). While we have not usually focused on patient satisfaction with care provided for specific diseases, some organizations are systematically including satisfaction assessments in their measurement program for high-priority clinical problems (e.g., care of women with breast cancer). As a result, we can begin to accumulate a database of knowledge about what most affects patient satisfaction for a variety of clinical conditions and of the specific opportunities available for improving care processes to meet patients' expectations.

A key element in caregiving is the physician-patient relationship. Some of the important products of this relationship—effective patient education, truly informed consent, shared decision making—lead to patient compliance and are critical to successful treatment.[3] Although we often do not measure these aspects of quality, this is another area in which patients are clearly the best source of information. For example, only patients can tell us whether they felt adequately informed about their primary treatment choices for breast cancer and whether they were able to participate as much as they wanted in the decision-making process about their treatment. Asthmatics can tell us whether they think they know the triggers for their own asthma, whether they have been given enough information about how to manage their own treatment in various circumstances, and whether they use their medications as prescribed. At the heart of the physician-patient relationship is the quality of the interaction. We can measure the quality of these interactions and their impact on the success of treatment plans and, ultimately, on patients' health, by asking patients to tell us about the relationship and their interactions with their doctor.

Increasingly, we need to understand the impact of treatments on patients' functioning, well-being, and quality of life long after they have left our offices. For example, surgeons want to understand, eight weeks after hip replacement surgery, how far patients are able to walk; cardiologists are interested in the frequency and severity of chest pain after revascularization; purchasers want to assess the value of care for depression by documenting how much time employees are missing work due to their illnesses.

Patients actively engage in behavior that may enhance, maintain, or limit their own health. Prevention, health promotion, and risk modification are part of many basic health plan strategies. To monitor the effectiveness of these programs and to identify opportunities for promoting health and wellness in populations, we need to assess risk factors and health-related behaviors (e.g., exercise, diet, smoking, alcohol consumption). Some health maintenance organizations routinely survey new members at or before their first encounters to identify at the outset opportunities for prevention, health promotion, and risk reduction.

As they travel through the health care system seeking symptom relief or reassurance, patients accumulate and integrate their experiences. Right now, very little quality measurement activity focuses on coordination of care provided to patients either across specialties (e.g., pediatrics and ENT), sites (e.g., clinic, laboratory, emergency department, hospital floor), or providers (e.g., primary care physician and orthopedic PA). Even multiple encounters within 24 hours involving different providers in the same department can result in uncoordinated and discontinuous care experiences for patients.

Imagine that a patient with poorly localized abdominal pain is seen in an emergency department at 11 p.m. After an examination, the physician diagnoses acute indigestion and prescribes antacid. When the patient returns at 7 a.m. doubled over in intense pain, it is apparent that the previous diagnosis needs reevaluation. As evaluation proceeds and several physicians become involved, the patient may become confused about who is in charge, who will make treatment decisions, and whether his or her own physician has been consulted. Later, when the pain is localized to the right lower quadrant, both the medical problem and the course of treatment are clear. Definitive treatment will be arranged, with the patient's input regarding choice of surgeon and postoperative follow up. Once discharged, the patient can tell us whether he or she understands the next steps in care, what warning signs to watch for, and when to resume different activities. A review of the episode of care with this or similar patients will be rich in unmet expectations that could be used to improve the quality of the process.

The Patient as the Most Efficient Source of Data

Broadly distributed organizations (e.g., large IPAs) often depend on claims data to address quality measurement. However, this information is often inaccurate, lacking in specificity, and only available long after services have been provided. Many organizations track mammography screening rates, C-section rates, and immunization rates by reviewing claims or charts. But it is often impossible to differentiate a primary C-section from a repeat C-section after a failed VBAC attempt on the basis of claims data. A detailed chart review would be necessary to capture this information. Yet, it is quite easy to ask women whether they delivered by C-section, whether they had one before, and whether they attempted to deliver vaginally. Assuming the survey produces accurate information (which should be demonstrated in a validity study), using patients to report on these experiences would be more efficient. The national Health Interview Survey has traditionally used this approach in collecting data about a variety of health experiences on an ongoing basis. There is little reason not to consider using this methodology when it is accurate and more cost-effective than other data collection strategies.

It is also often more efficient to gather information from patients as an alternative to gathering data from multiple sources. To continue the obstetrical example, if one also wanted to know about the quality of prenatal care (e.g., number of visits, tests, prenatal counseling, childbirth education) and women's satisfaction with labor and delivery, it makes sense to consider a single survey rather than a measurement approach that would involve a survey, a review of inpatient charts, and a review of outpatient obstetrical charts. The patient's ability to recall and report information about the broad spectrum of experiences associated with patient care makes such surveys rich and efficient information sources.

Asthma Quality Measurement at Harvard Community Health Plan

Asthma quality measurement at the Harvard Community Health Plan (HCHP) provides an ongoing example of the use of patient-based methods for assessing quality. Like many managed care organizations, HCHP has focused considerable effort on improving the care provided to adult asthmatics. The origin of this initiative lies in the availability of national guidelines and increasing media attention on asthma, as well as our own data on asthma-related hospital utilization. To monitor and improve performance in treating asthma according to recommended guidelines, physicians want information on therapies, patient self-treatment practices, symptoms, functional status, and patient satisfaction, as well as traditional utilization data. While information about utilization can be derived from claims, medication data are recorded in charts and pharmacy databases. Information about patient compliance with recommended therapies, self-management (e.g., knowledge and avoidance of asthma triggers, home peak flow monitoring), symptoms, functional status, and patient satisfaction can only be obtained from patients. We decided to rely on claims for utilization data and to obtain the remaining information through patient surveys, thereby avoiding the added burden of conducting chart review in a delivery system with more than 100 clinics and offices.

A pilot study on a relatively small sample helped to refine and shorten the questionnaire to focus on the following measures for moderate and severe adult asthmatics:

- Percentage prescribed inhaled steroids.

- Percentage using inhaled steroids daily.

- Percentage with written treatment plans developed with their clinicians for managing medications at home.

- Percentage prescribed and using home peak flow meters.

- Percentage who canceled or rearranged daily activities in the past month or missed work time because of asthma.

- Percentage satisfied or very satisfied with the care they have received for their asthma over the past six months.

In addition, we collected data on frequency and chronicity of various symptoms to classify patients by severity of asthma according to criteria defined by the guidelines. In 1993, we surveyed more than 8,000 adult asthmatics and collected claims-based utilization data to provide asthma performance results for each of approximately 40 sites within the HCHP network.

Since the survey, clinicians have been working to implement a variety of patient education, clinician education, and system improvement initiatives to improve on the different measures of performance. They have set performance targets, and a follow up measurement was conducted late in 1994 and early 1995. Results of the follow-up measurement revealed marked improvement in the use of inhaled steriods and home peak flow meters, as well as a decline in hospital days, among other changes. In this case, relying on patient experiences has enabled us to build an efficient quality information system to support asthma management efforts that should not only help reduce utilization but also improve patient compliance, self-treatment, functioning, and satisfaction.

Challenges in Patient-Based Measurement

The field of patient-based quality measurement is evolving. Increasingly, journals and conferences on quality of care and improvement focus on insights into patient-based measurement issues and strategies. Researchers and quality measurement staff are constantly developing new tools and techniques to tap previously unmeasured aspects of health services from the patient's perspective. Substantive research reveals that patients' involvement in their own health care decisions mediates the impact of medical treatments, making it even more critical to understand the patient perspective and the impact of patient involvement in medical care.

A patient-based quality measurement program needs to be integrated into a complete quality measurement strategy. Three key issues should guide any effort to implement patient-based quality measurement. First, the effort should focus on *key patient needs and expectations, assessing quality in language familiar to patients.* For example, employees in health care organizations talk about *access.* Patients talk about seeing the doctors they want, where they want to see them, and at times that are convenient for them. The real value of patient-reported quality measurement is the ability to describe the quality of health care from the customer's perspective. The best approach to understanding their concerns on their terms is to spend time talking about the issues with patients, using focus groups and interviews. A complementary strategy is to review patient complaint calls and letters.

Second, data collection should *rely on the best available tools.* It is much easier to ask a question poorly than to ask it in a way that will provide accurate, reliable, and valid information. Fortunately, new tools are being developed every day. Many health care organizations devote their own internal resources to development of quality measurement tools. Scanning the literature and benchmarking other organizations is often a more efficient approach for identifying measurement instruments than designing them locally. It also has the advantage of performance comparisons with other organizations using the same instrument.

Because it is often difficult to identify the best tool for a specific need or because the application of a survey is different from the one used in developing it (e.g., different population, different data collection methodology), it is critical to pilot-test surveys. It is quite efficient to use small samples to test surveys to ensure that respondents understand the questions, that the survey will be completed, and that responses will provide the information you desire. Often, focus groups or cognitive interviews are necessary to verify that respondents understand and respond to questions as intended. The small investment of time and resources required to pilot-test and refine a survey is usually far less than the potential wasted cost of obtaining poor quality or useless data and minimizes the risk of burdening or irritating large numbers of respondents with unnecessary questions.

Finally, no health care organization today can afford to be inefficient in its data collection efforts. To achieve the best value for the measurement dollar, the data collection methodology should be designed for the specific application. Data collection methodologies vary from standard paper and pencil surveys administered on-site in health care organizations by delivery system staff, to telephone surveys administered by trained interviewers, to mailed surveys administered by research staff. Each of these methodologies has advantages and limitations both in costs and response rates. For quality measurement purposes, the challenge is to *optimize response rate* while using a cost-effective data collection strategy given the objectives and available staff and resources. In many instances, you may not need a high response rate to begin to evaluate quality. For example, if a survey of adult asthmatics results in a 50 percent response rate and reveals that only 60 percent of severe asthmatic respondents have received a prescription for inhaled steroids, the most optimistic assessment of the potential response bias (i.e., all of the remaining 40 percent had received a prescription) would still lead you to conclude that at least 20 percent of severe asthmatics *had not* received a prescription. For many purposes, this is adequate information to target improvement efforts.

For other objectives, it may be important to devote the resources required to approach research quality response rates (i.e., over 80 to 90 percent). For example, if individual physician compensation were determined in part by measurable improvement in patient satisfaction, most physicians would want to be sure that respondents accurately represented the population of patients under their care. Substantial resources could be dedicated to ensuring a high response rate (e.g., follow up reminders and mailings, telephone interviews) or in thoroughly evaluating nonrespondent bias. Similarly, in evaluating the outcomes of new treatments or programs, it is often important to obtain a thorough assessment of their impact. One could imagine a new program to reduce repeat Cesarean deliveries and increase VBAC rates. Part of the evaluation might involve surveying mothers at six weeks postpartum to assess functional status and satisfaction. If mothers who responded to the survey were satisfied and doing fine, but the response rate was only 40 percent, most physician managers would want to know whether the remaining nonrespondents were precisely those women who were experiencing functional impairments and were dissatisfied with the program.

The measurement objective should also partially determine the data collection methodology. If the measurement goal requires recall of specific experiences (e.g., how long did you wait in the exam room? Did the medical assistant address you by name when calling you into the office? Were you given clear written instructions before you left the hospital?), the data should be gathered near the time of the experience, ideally by telephone rather than mail. If you are seeking general information about care that took place over time, a mailed survey will be both adequate and less costly. Many technologies are now emerging that should help minimize the costs of data collection and analysis and make patient-reported quality measurement much easier. These include scannable surveys that can be read and analyzed by inexpensive machines; touch screens, similar to automatic bank teller machines, that can be used on site in health care organizations; and voice-administered telephone surveys that capture data instantly in readily accessible databases.

Summary

Patient-based quality measurement covers a broad spectrum of content and requires substantial methodological and operational expertise, but it is well within the capabilities of most health care organizations. Some prioritization is essential to focus patient-based quality measurement on areas of greatest clinical and strategic interest. Drawing on the best available tools and strategies and incorporating the voice of the patient in quality measurement will result in improved quality of care and increased patient satisfaction.

References

1. Nelson, E. "Patient-Based Quality Measurement Systems." *Quality Management in Health Care* 2(1):18-30, Fall 1993.

2. Davies, A., and Ware, J. "Involving Consumers in Quality of Care Assessment: Do They Provide Valid Information?" *Health Affairs* 7(1):33-48, Spring 1988.

3. Greenfield, S., and others. "Patients Participation in Medical Care: Effects on Blood Sugar Control and Quality of Life in Diabetes." *Journal of General Internal Medicine* 3(5):448-57, Sept.-Oct. 1988.

Acknowledgments

The development of this chapter and the conceptual and empirical work on which it is based were supported in part by the Harvard Community Health Plan Foundation.

CHAPTER 12

Feedback of Clinical Performance Information*

by Stephen C. Schoenbaum, MD, MPH

Introduction

Health care organizations are increasingly being asked to provide information on their performance to their customers. This is particularly true in the HMO industry, where performance data requests by employers are commonplace. Recently, an attempt to standardize some of these data requests across organizations has led to the development and implementation of HEDIS, the Health Plan Employer Data and Information Set (see chapter 5). Both employers and members expect that HMOs, which hold themselves forth as managing care, will not just measure their performance but also progressively improve it. This raises the question of how one can translate information into action and performance improvement. The terms "practice profiles," or just "profiles," refer to the types of clinical performance information HMOs are producing for internal use and to satisfy the requests of their customers. The process of translating performance information into action requires as a critical, indeed essential, first step feedback of data. This chapter sets out a framework for understanding feedback of measurements, the direct influence of feedback on clinical performance, and the desirability of linking feedback to an overall quality management process to ensure better performance.

Case Example of Profiling and Feedback

It will be instructive to begin with an example: For the past several years the corporate medical director's office at Harvard Community Health Plan (HCHP) has been measuring adult screening practices by reviewing a random sample of medical records of persons who have been continuous members for at least one year. Some of the results are shown in figures 1 through 3, pages 106 and 107. HCHP has three HMO divisions, two staff models (HCD = Health Centers Division, NED = New England Division) and one group-network model (MGD = Medical Groups Division). The 1992 and 1993 measurements demonstrate similar results in all three divisions. In MGD, there was particularly

---

* Adapted with permission from an article in *HMO Practice* by the author.

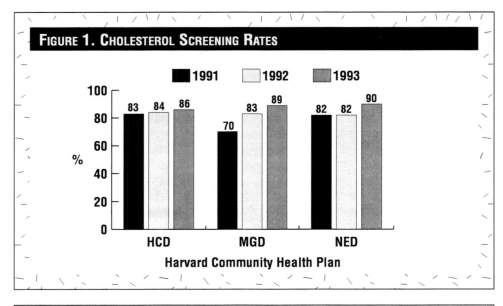

FIGURE 1. CHOLESTEROL SCREENING RATES

Harvard Community Health Plan

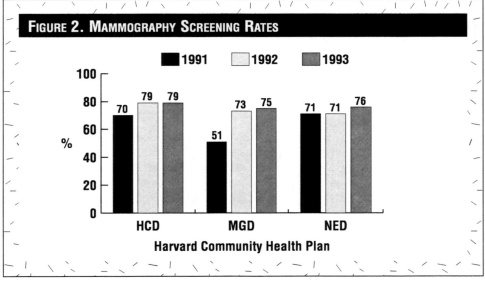

FIGURE 2. MAMMOGRAPHY SCREENING RATES

Harvard Community Health Plan

strong improvement in all three screening practices between the 1991 and 1992 measurements. In order to interpret these data, it is important to know that, each year, information on performance has been returned, or fed back, to the medical directors of each of the 11 independent medical groups in MGD that contract with HCHP. The comments of these medical directors have suggested that much of the improvement in the results of MGD is related to the feedback. The medical directors report that they believe the information has focused attention on these screening practices because they are being

Measuring Clinical Care: A Guide for Physician Executives

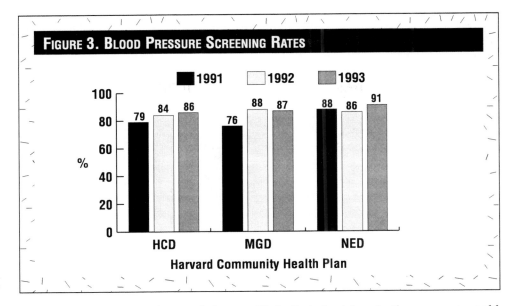

FIGURE 3. BLOOD PRESSURE SCREENING RATES

measured. That, in turn, has made it more likely that physicians in these groups would either perform the screen or be sure to document it. In short, this is just one example of the fact that feedback of information about clinical practices can exert an extremely powerful influence on those practices.

Types of Feedback and a Review of Its Effects

There are three basic ways to feed measurement information back to physicians or HMOs. Peer comparison feedback consists of reporting performance back to an individual physician or group along with comparative data from others. Individual feedback consists of providing an individual physician or group information about its own performance without providing comparative information. Grouped or aggregate feedback involves providing individual physicians with information on the performance of the larger group of which they are a part, but not providing them with their own individual information.

Peer comparison feedback is usually meaningful as long as the individual or group agrees that the comparative data that have been provided truly represent data from peers (i.e., that what is being compared is truly comparable). In contrast, individual feedback is meaningful only if there is a clear norm or standard for performance, so that the individual physician or group can assess its own performance in relation to that norm. For example, a physician who is told that he or she failed to give MMR to 10 percent of infants who were seen for a well-baby check at 15 months of age can probably interpret the data without any information about peers, because there is a performance norm indicated in official immunization recommendations. However, a physician who is told that his or her rate of ordering chest x-rays was 28.7 per 1000 encounters probably cannot interpret the data, because there is no obvious norm.

Similarly, aggregate feedback is meaningful only if the individuals within the group can relate their own performance to that of the group as a whole or to a clear norm or standard. One study that has been cited to demonstrate that feedback is not an effective mechanism for improving performance was a randomized controlled trial of interventions designed to increase the rates of VBAC (vaginal birth after cesarean section) and to decrease the rates of repeat cesarean section among groups of obstetricians.[1] This is one of the few published studies in which aggregate or group feedback has been used without a clear norm; and it simply did not work, i.e., no change in performance occurred. In contrast, when HCHP's Health Centers Division wanted to encourage physicians to convert patients who were taking enalapril to lisinopril, a first step was to provide information to each physician about his or her health center's use of enalapril instead of lisinopril. Because initially no center was near 100 percent usage of lisinopril (the implied norm), most physicians could readily identify that they, as individuals, had opportunities for conversion of patients. Only later, as the group's use of lisinopril versus enalapril started to go up and individuals could no longer identify with the aggregate data, was it necessary to begin to supply individual information.

In early 1992, we reviewed the literature and found almost 50 published studies involving the feedback of practice profiles.[2] The results are summarized in table 1, below.

TABLE 1. PERFORMANCE IMPROVEMENT IN PUBLISHED STUDIES INVOLVING FEEDBACK OF PRACTICE PROFILE INFORMATION

Category	Number of Studies in Category	Number with Performance Improvement	Percentage with Performance Improvement
All studies	48	39	81%
Controlled trials	26	20	77%
Type of Feedback			
Peer comparison	5*	4	80%
Individual	10*	8	80%
Aggregate	3*	2	67%
Physicians studied			
House staff	17	14	82%
Practitioners	24	20	83%
Both	7	5	71%
Improvement tools			
Feedback alone	10*	7	70%
Feedback in combination	15*	12	80%
Study objective			
Increase utilization	7*	7	100%
Decrease utilization or cost	19*	13	68%
* Controlled trials			

They demonstrate that feedback can, and usually does, improve performance. It did so in 81 percent of all studies reviewed, including almost 80 percent of all the controlled trials. Success has been reported for all types of feedback, but less often for the handful of studies using aggregate or grouped feedback than for individual or peer comparison feedback. As already mentioned, these studies of aggregate feedback did not necessarily provide a norm or standard of comparison that would have made measurements more meaningful. We did find that success has been reported in most studies involving practicing physicians, not just house staff in teaching hospital settings. Feedback does appear to be somewhat more successful when used in combination with other performance enhancers, such as education about the topic being measured, rewards, or use of opinion leaders to disseminate the message to other practitioners. Finally, the review indicates that feedback has been more effective when the objective has been to enhance utilization—e.g., immunization or screening—than when the objective has been to reduce utilization or costs. Nevertheless, simple feedback of information on practices can be, and usually is, effective in reducing utilization or costs.

Obtaining "Buy-In" to Clinical Performance Information

For information about practice performance, or a "practice profile," to have an impact, physicians must "buy in" to the profile. Physicians are most likely to "buy in" if the information in the profile is meaningful. Both the content of the profile and the process by which the information is fed back can enhance the meaningfulness of profiles and the likelihood of "buy-in." Table 2, below, summarizes the issues involved in enhancing the meaningfulness of profiles that will be discussed below.

It is indisputable that one way to achieve "buy-in" is to employ well-accepted scientific principles as a basis for profiling. This becomes a rationale for basing profiles on practice guidelines that, in turn, are supported by the scientific literature (evidence-based

TABLE 2. FACTORS RELATING TO THE CONTENT OF PROFILES AND PROCESS OF FEEDBACK THAT INCREASE PHYSICIAN "BUY IN"	
Content	**Process**
Deriving measurements from evidence-based or consensus-based guidelines	Obtaining physician participation in the development of measurements
Producing and providing accurate, auditable data	Convening physicians or encouraging their participation in the interpretation of profiles
Providing statistically stable data	
Adjusting for case-mix, as appropriate	
Supplying actionable information (process vs. outcome)	

guidelines) or by accepted clinical rules (consensus-based guidelines). Thus, when HCHP's medical directors fed back mammography results, they were building on the fact that three HCHP divisions had previously approved a set of mammography guidelines that were based on national guidelines.

When profile information, such as utilization information, does not derive from a scientific base, its content value still may be enhanced by making sure that it is as free as possible from measurement error. It may sound simplistic to recommend that data be accurate and auditable, but, unfortunately, this is often a difficult condition to meet, given the poor quality of information about clinical practice. Everyone knows that it is difficult to get detailed clinical information. It often requires abstraction from records or special surveys, and, usually, the easier it is to get the data, the poorer the data are. It is not unreasonable for physicians to question the accuracy of the data; unfortunately, they often are not accurate. Physicians generally are willing to accept audited data, even if their measurement is not based on some scientific fact or national norm.

Physicians are more likely to "buy in" to information if they believe it is statistically stable. When one sees performance data based on very small numbers, the first question that comes to mind is whether the differences that purported to be demonstrated by the data are due to chance alone.[3] If a physician has good reason to think that variations in the data are random, he or she is not very likely to "buy in." Unfortunately, clinical data often are based on small numbers and are not statistically stable. One way to handle this problem is to follow the data over time and plot them in a time series. Figure 4, below, shows information on cesarean section rates for two HMOs. At any single point, it might be difficult to conclude that there was a meaningful difference in the rates of cesarean section in the two organizations. Nevertheless, an examination of the overall pattern of performance in the two HMOs over time leads one to the conclusion that the

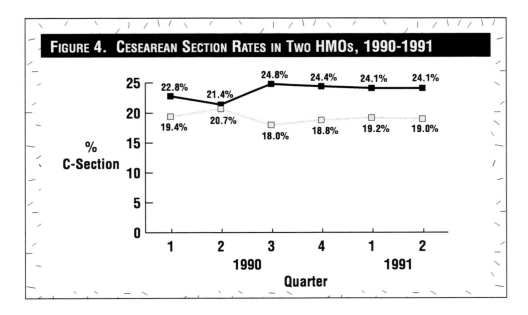

FIGURE 4. CESEAREAN SECTION RATES IN TWO HMOS, 1990-1991

Measuring Clinical Care: A Guide for Physician Executives

reported rates are truly different for the two organizations. In other words, there is a significant difference between the two performance curves over time, even if there isn't a significant difference at any of the individual points in time.

A second question that usually arises when comparative clinical performance data are presented is whether observed differences in performance are actually due to differences in "case mix" or population differences rather than to differences in performance for similar populations. Case-mix adjustment or risk adjustment can be a difficult task (see Chapter 10). It obviously can make a difference in the results, but, interestingly, it often does not make *much* of a difference. Returning to the information in figure 4, assume that the persons who are supplying the information can ensure that the two HMOs are serving similar populations and that the data have been collected similarly in the two organizations. With those two assurances, it should be possible for physicians to "buy in" to the data and conclude that there is a difference in the process of care in these two organizations that leads to the difference in c-section rates.

Physicians also are more likely to "buy in" to information about clinical performance that is "actionable." Information about process of care is more likely to be acted upon than information about outcomes. When physicians are given information about or closely related to their processes of care, such as mammography rates, it is relatively easy to act upon the data. In contrast, when physicians are given outcomes data, which usually result from a complex process or set of processes, it is not obvious what is needed to improve outcomes. The data alone do not indicate an appropriate action step. For example, even if one agrees with the conclusion from the data in figure 2 that differences in the processes of care are likely to be leading to the differences in c-section rates, it is not obvious just what needs to be to done in managing the processes of pregnancy and labor to change the results. Identifying the specific processes or process changes that might improve the outcome is a complicated task, but one that is essential if physicians are truly going to manage care.

Two process issues that may be related to the effectiveness of feedback are participation in the development of profiles and interaction in the feedback step. Although it may not be absolutely necessary to enlist physician participation in the development of profiles and feedback information, it is highly desirable to do so, especially if the profile information does not derive from scientifically demonstrated medical facts. Physician involvement is likely to influence the format and the content of the information obtained and delivered as feedback. As with the development of clinical guidelines or algorithms, participation is usually fun and almost always educational.

Having physicians participate as a group in interpretation of the profiles appears to enhance the effectiveness of feedback. The work of the Maine Medical Assessment Foundation[4] provides an interesting example. This group has adopted techniques of small-area analysis developed originally by John Wennberg and his colleagues at Dartmouth Medical School and has used them as a basis for obtaining information for feedback and peer involvement of physicians. Figure 5, page 112, illustrates the discovery by the Orthopaedic Study Group that there was an increase in the number of lumbar disc operations in Maine in 1983 and 1984 versus the period of 1980 through 1982. This proved to be attributable to one small area that had had a lower than average number of excisions in the earlier period followed by a dramatic rise. Information on the

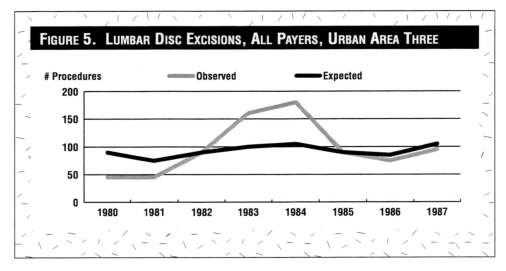

FIGURE 5. LUMBAR DISC EXCISIONS, ALL PAYERS, URBAN AREA THREE

variation in lumbar disc excision rates was presented to, and discussed by, a statewide group of orthopedists and neurosurgeons in a feedback meeting in early 1985. The increased rate in the one area appeared to be attributable to three new surgeons who had begun practicing in the area. The statewide meeting presumably clarified accepted indications or criteria for surgery, because the rate in the previously high area promptly fell to the state average.

One can picture similar events occurring in large group practices or hospital practices when new physicians are hired. They may simply not be "acculturated" to the group's usual modes of practice and may have utilization patterns different from those of the rest of the group. The acculturation process is more likely to occur rapidly if there is more organized and directed discussion of clinical performance between older and newer physicians across systems of care. Interestingly, in the study on lumbar disc operations in Maine, not only did the outlier area change its practice after the meeting, but also there was a decrease in the overall variation in performance around the state. So the effects of bringing together groups of older and newer physicians in a group practice may not be confined to the newer physicians.

All told, group participation in interpreting clinical performance information seems to help alter such performance. Group participation can occur only if the party that has the information convenes the group. Unfortunately, there have been many lost opportunities for convening groups to understand clinical data. This has occurred even on a national level, such as when HCFA simply published mortality data for hospitals rather than bringing together diverse institutions to work on understanding the data. It is worth mentioning that another way of obtaining participation is to feed information back to physicians personally and to use an opinion leader in the feedback process.

Linking Feedback to Quality Management

Feedback can be educational—by getting feedback on one's performance compared to that of others, one may learn what sort of performance level is attainable. Feedback can

Measuring Clinical Care: A Guide for Physician Executives

also function as a positive incentive or reward by demonstrating to a clinician that his or her numbers have gotten better over time. Feedback can remind or prompt a clinician to perform certain tasks or processes. Unfortunately, sometimes the clinician may think that the information he or she is receiving has negative connotations and may feel "flogged by the data." Nevertheless, it still may spur the physician to perform better in order to avoid further "punishment."

John Eisenberg has summarized the factors that alter physician performance.[5] Each of the roles of feedback mentioned above—education, reminder, and positive and negative incentives—is known to be a modifier of physician performance in its own right, and sometimes feedback is used in combination with other performance modifiers, including specific educational interventions, reminders, prompts, notifications, and various rewards and punishments.

There are several rationales or hypotheses to explain why feedback alone might lead physicians to improve performance. One is that, when physicians see new information, they will change their previous beliefs, and this ultimately will lead to a change in actions. A second is that physicians cannot accurately assess their own practices without specific information. Thus, only when specific information is provided can the physician understand what he or she is actually doing and change. Another hypothesis is based on the notion that physicians are highly motivated to change and are extremely competitive. This hypothesis indicates that, when physicians are given some information about their own performance in relation to that of others or to a norm and believe the information or find it meaningful, they will promptly change their practices in order to meet or beat the competition.

Whichever hypothesis might be accurate, feedback alone can be considered a form of exhortation. Although exhortation works up to a point, it requires a lot of energy and often doesn't lead to lasting effects. Obtaining practice profiles, feeding them back, and convening groups to understand them and the underlying processes of care are just first steps. To achieve exceptional performance, these first steps must be linked explicitly to interventions that specify and then manage or control the process of care.

In the future there is likely to be a substantial increase in measurement or profiling of clinical performance. There are two reasons for this conclusion:

- The increasing demand from the public for more accountability in health care.

- An increasing recognition by persons within the health care industry, including some physicians, that significant quality problems and opportunities for improvement do exist.

Up to now, many practice profiles have been generated just because the data are there. That is not the most productive basis on which to proceed. Instead, in the design of the profiles or measurements of care, it is essential to focus on what data are needed and why they are needed. This issue must be considered at all levels of the health care delivery system. It is critical to state hypotheses about care processes and outcomes and have goals for data collection. In turn, the hypotheses will shape the design of systems to facilitate the collection of appropriate data and the analysis of those data into the required information.

It is likely that the process just outlined will entail the development and enhancement of automated clinical information systems, but much relevant clinical data can be collected manually. For example, some years ago, prior to the development of endocervical brushes for obtaining endocervical cytology specimens, an internist at HCHP, Roberta Herman, organized her local department of medicine to study whether adoption of a single standardized method of obtaining Pap smears could improve the rate of recovery of endocervical cells. The group agreed to the method, and, by working with the health center's laboratory, it was possible to obtain the data on endocervical cell recovery before and after the intervention. There was a significant improvement that was maintained until the introduction of endocervical brushes, a practice that brought about yet another quantum improvement.

Opportunities abound for assessing and improving care. Feedback of performance information can often make a difference in and of itself. It is a gross mistake to hoard data rather than giving them back to people who can use them. When groups are convened to react to feedback, one can stimulate a discussion that will lead to process specification and improvement. It is likely that physicians and their patients will benefit from this.

References

1. Lomas, J., and others. "Opinion Leaders vs. Audit and Feedback to Implement Practice Guidelines: Delivery after Previous Cesarean Section." *JAMA* 265(17):2202-7, May 1, 1991.

2. Schoenbaum, S., and Murrey, K: "Impact of profiles on Medical Practice." *Proceedings of Conference on Profiling,* 1992. Physician Payment Review Commission, 92-2:71-125.

3. Halvorson, G., and others. "The Myth of Micro-Data." *HMO Practice* 5(5):178-82, Sept.-Oct. 1991.

4. Caper, P. "Population-Based Measures of the Quality of Medical Care." In Couch, J., Ed., *Health Care Quality Management for the 21st Century.* Tampa, Fla.: American College of Physician Executives, 1991, pp.281-327.

5. Eisenberg, J. *Doctors' Decisions and the Cost of Medical Care: The Reasons for Doctors' Practice Patterns and Ways to Change Them.* Ann Arbor, Mich.: Health Administration Press, 1986.

Designing and Executing Experiments in Care— A Data-Driven, Scientific Approach to Quality Improvement

by Frederic G. Jones, MD, FACPE and Colletta H. (K.K.) Moore, MS

lumenthal informed us that increasing concern about the quality of health care has led to the deployment of many new techniques designed to monitor, compare, and improve the clinical performance of health care providers.[1] The most popular seems to be the basic tenets of what is called industrial quality management science (IQMS), also known as statistical quality improvement. Some of the most common statistical quality improvement techniques have been easily adapted in the health care setting (see Chapter 9). Such techniques currently used to study performance or outcomes include flow charts, cause-and-effect diagrams, Pareto charts, and run charts. Although substantial improvement can be obtained using these basic tools, often the process is still not capable. That is, customer needs may still not be met, or practitioners' expectations are not being fulfilled for their patients. Going "beyond the basics," Anderson Area Medical Center (AAMC), a private, not-for-profit, 587-bed facility located in Anderson, South Carolina, recognizes that design of experiments should play an integral role in process improvement.[2]

In health care, we have traditionally used experimentation to further our knowledge. Many observational and local trials of single interventions have been conducted in the past, and some of them have led to sustained quality improvement. For example, an experiment was conducted at AAMC using an experimental group and a control group of physicians to improve processes and practice for its practitioners.[3,4] The experimental variable consisted of a one-time exposure of physicians to clinical and financial specifics regarding their individual treatment and management of pneumonia patients. It was found that providing physicians with specific feedback about their practice behavior resulted in their using fewer resources as expressed in total billed charges and length of stay (see Chapter 12). At the same time, there was no compromise in outcomes for patients as measured by mortality, readmission rates, and infection/complication rates. This improvement in resource utilization was observed for two years following the provision of practice-specific data to the experimental physicians.

The type of experimentation discussed in this chapter, however, involves the testing of *multiple* ideas *simultaneously* with minimal experimentation costs. The fallacy of holding conditions constant to observe the effects of a particular factor on an outcome is just that, a fallacy. By testing many factors or ideas at once through a well-planned, statistics-based, experimental design, significant individual factors can be uncovered, as well as the *combinations* of factors that significantly affect the outcome. These interactions of factors cannot be found experimenting with one factor at a time.

In the remainder of this chapter, we will discuss the preliminary work that is required for designing and executing an experiment, demonstrate the power of the technique through the discussion of two case studies, and, most important, stress the implications behind applying this technique to achieve process breakthroughs in clinical care.

Preliminary Work Required

Stability, or predictability, is a prerequisite to experimental design. Design of experiments (DOE) is never intended to replace traditional quality improvement techniques. Rather, its suggested use comes after the known, uncontrollable sources of variation have been studied and removed. Therefore, DOE can be thought of as yet another technique in the quality improvement arsenal. Accordingly, AAMC uses QualPro's Eight-Step Procedure for Improving a Process©, the last step of which is DOE (see figure 1, page 117). The first three steps address "looking at the process." That is, the purpose of the process improvement effort is clearly defined, measures important to the external customer are clearly defined, and the measurement systems in place to obtain the pertinent data are assessed for accuracy and precision.

Step 4 of the Eight-Step Procedure assesses stability of the process by using a control chart technique that distinguishes between uncontrollable, or special cause variation, and inherent variation, also known as common cause variation (figure 2, page 117). The control chart provides a frequency distribution with an added dimension of time. Control limits are usually set at three standard deviations above and below the mean of an item being measured. Special cause variation would be evident with events occurring above and below the control limits. These events would be highly unlikely to occur simply by chance and thus would indicate unexpected outcomes. Special cause variation is also evident if the control chart reveals unusual patterns of events even when outcome measurements are within control limits. In a clinical context, special cause variation describes epidemic occurrences (i.e., the number of cases exceeds that expected on the basis of past experience). Common cause variation describes endemic occurrences (i.e., number of cases based on past experience within a given population).[5]

In addition to detecting special and common cause variations, a control chart also permits managers, team members, and even casual observers (internal customers such as physicians) to note the process under study in real time. This facilitates our focusing not upon individual cases and discrete events, but upon systems and trends. Berwick writes that physicians as well as practitioners of the quality sciences "recognize how crucial the appropriate interpretation of variation is to wise action."[6] Therefore, sharing such data-driven and graphically displayed information with a group of clinicians avoids attribution and focuses on identifying opportunities for improvement in the process. Blumenthal gives numerous clinical applications of control charts.[1] A few additional

Measuring Clinical Care: A Guide for Physician Executives

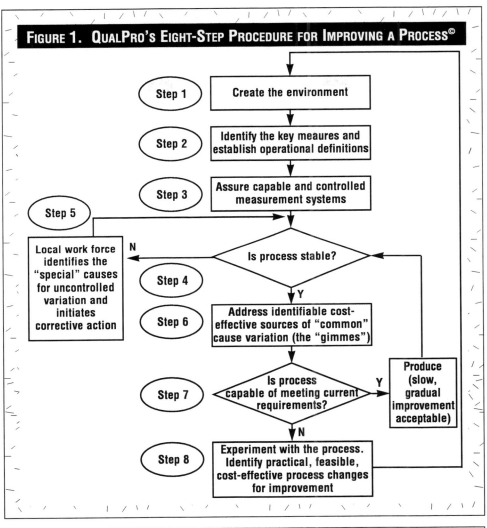

FIGURE 1. QUALPRO'S EIGHT-STEP PROCEDURE FOR IMPROVING A PROCESS©

Step 1 — Create the environment

Step 2 — Identify the key meaures and establish operational definitions

Step 3 — Assure capable and controlled measurement systems

Step 4 — Is process stable?

Step 5 — Local work force identifies the "special" causes for uncontrolled variation and initiates corrective action

Step 6 — Address identifiable cost-effective sources of "common" cause variation (the "gimmes")

Step 7 — Is process capable of meeting current requirements?

Produce (slow, gradual improvement acceptable)

Step 8 — Experiment with the process. Identify practical, feasible, cost-effective process changes for improvement

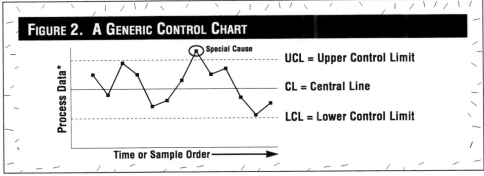

FIGURE 2. A GENERIC CONTROL CHART

Special Cause

UCL = Upper Control Limit

CL = Central Line

LCL = Lower Control Limit

Process Data*

Time or Sample Order ⟶

examples include patient dissatisfaction, turnaround time on radiology reports, and door-to-needle time for acute myocardial infarction patients.

Once special cause variation is detected, it should be eliminated prior to a planned and executed experiment. Step 5 of the Eight-Step Procedure further suggests that the local work force, or caregivers, have the knowledge and are best able to explain and remove special cause variation. Also, standardization of the process is addressed in Step 5. Once the process is stable and predictable, some things about the process become obvious and should be changed. These obvious process changes should be implemented prior to experimentation at Step 6 of the Eight-Step Procedure. That is, if statistical evidence is present that indicates a process change will positively affect an outcome, immediate implementation reduces experimentation costs. An example of an obvious process change is elimination of redundancies and other non-value-added activity. Elimination of tampering, the costly, inappropriate intervening on a process, is another obvious process change. Tampering is sometimes detected on a control chart through rapid swings back and forth in the data. Once the preliminary work to experimentation is completed, the control chart is also effective in evaluating the process after interventions have taken place, as shown in the two case studies that follow.

Two Case Studies
In 1992, AAMC began to examine and work to improve two areas of care: patient dissatisfaction with emergency services[2] and turnaround time for radiology reports.[7]

Patient Dissatisfaction with Emergency Services
The preliminary work required to experiment with patient dissatisfaction with emergency services began with the establishment of an ongoing measurement system. Each day, a telephone survey was administered to 40 randomly selected discharged emergency patients. A control chart graphically displayed the proportion of dissatisfied patients each day (figure 3, page 119). Initially, on any given day, a dissatisfaction rate as high as 47 percent would not have been an unusual event. We discovered a change in physician scheduling removed a source of special cause variation. Dramatic improvement resulted, with an average dissatisfaction rate of 8 percent. The process was stable; therefore, experimentation was possible.

Factors that were studied in the experiment included the presence of a fast track system for nonemergency patients; a follow-up call next day at home to the patient by an R.N.; a handout pamphlet explaining the emergency process and triage; a television in the waiting room; and cosmetic changes to the pediatric treatment room. These five factors are summarized in table 1, page 120. The team then used a Plackett-Burman experimental design[8] to test the five factors (table 2, page 120). A Plackett-Burman design is a type of experimental design used initially to evaluate a large number of factors and select from among them a smaller set of important factors for subsequent experimentation. Each row in table 2 defines a specific combination of factors that will be used for one experimental run. Analysis of the experimental results showed that the *combination* of fast track and the cosmetic changes to the pediatric treatment room had a statistically significant effect on patient dissatisfaction (figure 4, page 121). If the team had experimented with only one factor at a time, it would have drawn the erroneous conclusion

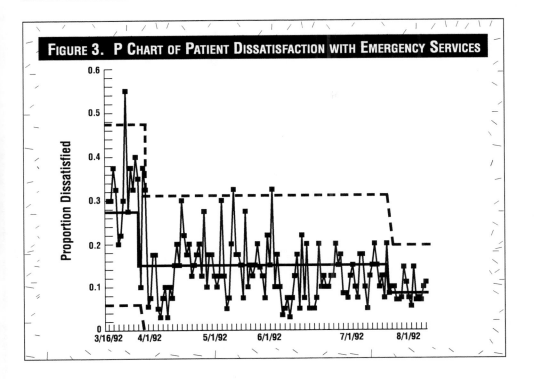

Figure 3. P Chart of Patient Dissatisfaction with Emergency Services

that patient dissatisfaction could not have been significantly reduced with the five factors that were tested. At present, patient dissatisfaction is running at less than 6 percent (figure 5, page 121).

The reader of this case study may infer that the removal of special cause variation is more significant than evaluating combinations of interventions to determine which are the most significant. However, we must stress again that the intended use of DOE comes after the removal of special cause variation and implementation of obvious process changes, not in place of them. DOE is the appropriate technique to use when the process is *still* not capable of meeting customer requirements.

Turnaround Time for Radiology Reports

Before designing and executing an experiment to reduce turnaround time for radiology reports, a team developed a measurement system to track the time from patient arrival until the time the transcription was sent. A control chart showed that, on average, the turnaround time was 12.31 hours. It would not be unusual, however, for the turnaround time to be as high as 22.97 hours (figure 6, page 122). After studying the uncontrollable sources of variation, the team learned that the special causes pointed to reports that had been requested on the nursing units before the film had been interpreted. An identification system was implemented that reduced the "film on floor" time and, thereby, reduced total turnaround time. The process became stable, with an average turnaround time of 5.9 hours.

Designing and Executing Experiments in Care

TABLE 1. FACTORS AND LEVELS FOR EMERGENCY SERVICES CASE STUDY

Factor		Level
A: Fast Track	–	*Current condition*
	+	Nonemergency patients will receive service in a separate, clinic area
B: Internal Operations	–	*Current condition*
	+	Follow-up call next day at home to patient by R.N.; communicate to patient at time of discharge that an attempt will be made to see the original doctor on follow-up visit; send stable patients upstairs to radiology for quicker x-ray response.
C: Triage Area Changes	–	*Current condition*
	+	Handout pamphlet explaining emergency department process and triage; place a solid partition between the two triage desks to allow for more privacy; hand out a "welcome" card with names of triage nurse, charge nurse, and nurse manager, as well as whom to call if there are any problems.
D: Outside Waiting Room	–	*Current condition*
	+	Student volunteer to staff emergency department waiting area to help families and maintain coffee pot; place television in waiting room.
E: Pediatric Changes	–	*Current condition*
	+	Give coloring books and crayons to children; play children's movies in pediatric treatment room; apply large Disney characters on wall.

TABLE 2. EIGHT-RUN PLACKETT-BURMAN DESIGN

Run	A	B	C	D	E	F	G
1	+	+	+	–	+	–	–
2	–	+	+	+	–	+	–
3	–	–	+	+	+	–	+
4	+	–	–	+	+	+	–
5	–	+	–	–	+	+	+
6	+	–	+	–	–	+	+
7	+	+	–	+	–	–	+
8	–	–	–	–	–	–	–

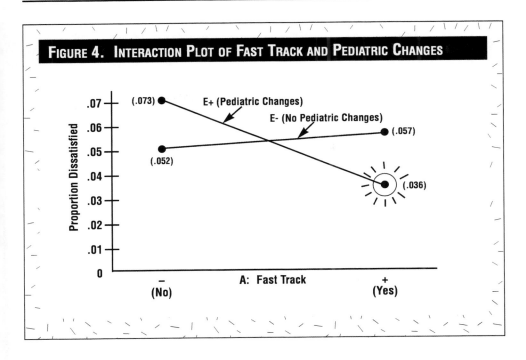

FIGURE 4. INTERACTION PLOT OF FAST TRACK AND PEDIATRIC CHANGES

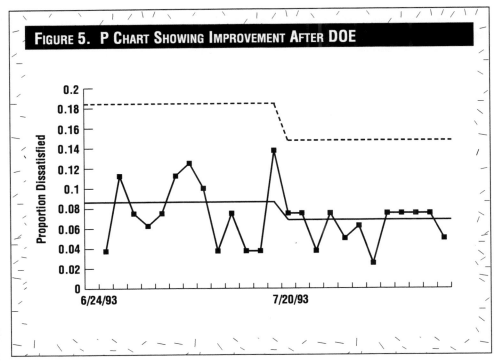

FIGURE 5. P CHART SHOWING IMPROVEMENT AFTER DOE

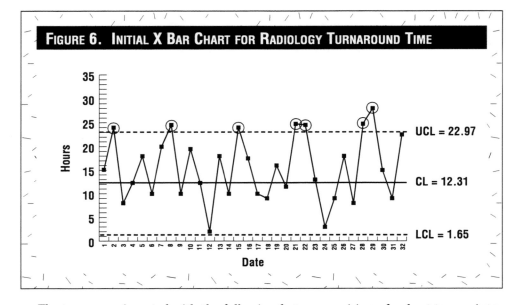

FIGURE 6. INITIAL X BAR CHART FOR RADIOLOGY TURNAROUND TIME

UCL = 22.97

CL = 12.31

LCL = 1.65

Hours

Date

The team experimented with the following factors: provision of a short-term printer that provided a process for obtaining the radiology folder before the current procedure was completed; a schedule board for tracking patients, staff, workload, etc.; combination of the film sorting and short-term file areas; provision of an additional full-time equivalent to serve as a "runner"; and elimination of the quality control function by allowing technologists to assume full responsibility and accountability for film quality. These five factors are summarized in table 3, page 123. The team used a 16-run Plackett-Burman design to decide which specific combinations of factors to test for in each experimental run (table 4, page 123). Without going into the detail of the calculations, the analysis showed that the combination of the schedule board and *no* runner significantly reduced total turnaround time (figure 7, page 124). This experiment illustrates a scientific approach to determine staffing levels. The results disproved the initial hypothesis that additional staffing was required to reduce turnaround time. To date, the average turnaround time is less than four hours.

Clearly, AAMC has enjoyed dramatic results through the use of experimental design. Although design of experiments has long been thought of as a tool to be used only in research and development labs and in improvement of manufacturing processes, its use in the health care industry can lead to process breakthrough.

Implications

Learning from its initial experience in the application of experimental design, AAMC has embarked on the journey of using the same data-driven, scientific approach to purely clinical processes. Like all other health care institutions, AAMC is interested in decreasing lengths of stay, costs, morbidity, and mortality and in improving clinical outcomes and patient satisfaction. Many organizations have made improvements in these areas through standardization of treatment among physicians. Through critical paths,

Measuring Clinical Care: A Guide for Physician Executives

TABLE 3. FACTORS AND LEVELS FOR RADIOLOGY CASE STUDY

Factor		Level
A. Short-Term Printer	–	Orders were not reprinted to short-term file area. Folders were searched for after the current procedure was performed.
	+	A short-term printer was simulated that provided a process for obtaining the radiology folder before the current procedure was completed.
B. Schedule Board	–	Schedule board was not utilized.
	+	A schedule board was used to provide an organized method for tracking patients, staff, work load, etc.
C. Sorting/Combo	–	Separate areas were utilized for film sorting and short-term filing.
	+	Combined film sorting and short-term file areas.
D. Runner	–	File room was staffed as usual.
	+	An additional person was employed on a temporary basis to transport films to and from various areas.
E. Quality Control (QC)	–	All routine films were routed through QC where a technologist rechecked all films for quality.
	+	QC was discontinued. Technologists assumed full responsibility and accountability for film quality.

TABLE 4. SIXTEEN-RUN PLACKETT-BURMAN DESIGN

Run	A	B	C	D	E
1	+	–	–	–	+
2	+	+	–	–	–
3	+	+	+	–	+
4	+	+	+	+	–
5	–	+	+	+	+
6	+	–	+	+	+
7	–	+	–	+	–
8	+	–	+	–	–
9	+	+	–	+	+
10	–	+	+	–	–
11	–	–	+	+	–
12	+	–	–	+	–
13	–	+	–	–	+
14	–	–	+	–	+
15	–	–	–	+	+
16	–	–	–	–	–

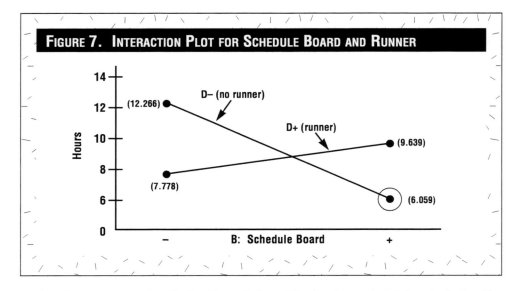

FIGURE 7. INTERACTION PLOT FOR SCHEDULE BOARD AND RUNNER

protocols, care-maps, etc., the best knowledge of the local experts is taken to design the most appropriate plans of care for a specific patient population. Numerous cases have been cited in which this type of activity has resulted in measurable improvement. However, in the context of experimental design, this type of activity is viewed as *preliminary work* to experimentation. As previously mentioned, standardization is often an obvious intervention that should be implemented prior to experimentation.

Furthermore, Berwick writes, "The surging interest in care guidelines, protocols, and so-called critical paths is a first-cousin to the TQM effort, but not always a welcome one."[6] Wouldn't physicians be more accepting of standard plans of care if they were based on a scientific, statistically based methodology as opposed to perhaps a governing body's ability to reach consensus? Experimental design techniques would make this possible. Consider the treatment of an acute myocardial infarction (AMI) patient. Should he receive specific education regarding the importance of shortening the treatment-seeking-decision-time, or is general community education sufficient? Should he be discharged on aspirin alone, or should he be discharged on aspirin and beta-blockers? Should he be given dietary teaching or not? Should the physician insist on cardiac rehabilitation or not? Should the patient be given pharmacy teaching or not? Should he be discharged from a specialized cardiac step-down unit, or is discharge from a general medical unit sufficient? Should in-house education be delivered in a written format or an oral format? The number of decisions that physicians are asked to make seems endless. Experimental design is one of the most powerful tools to provide the necessary answers.

The authors believe that experimental design techniques should and will be an integral part of a health care organization's continuous quality improvement effort. Testing multiple factors simultaneously can uncover breakthrough opportunities and is the only way to get at the most efficient combination of interventions.

Measuring Clinical Care: A Guide for Physician Executives

References

1. Blumenthal, D. "Total Quality Management and Physicians' Clinical Decisions." *JAMA* 269(21):2775–8, June 2, 1993.

2. Moore, C. "Experimental Design in Health Care." *Quality Management in Health Care* 2(2):13-26, Winter 1994.

3. Jones, F. "Education-Based Practice Pattern Analysis: A Tool for Continuous Improvement of Patient Care Quality." *American Journal of Medical Quality* 7:120-4, Winter 1993.

4. Johnson, C., and others. "The Effect of a Physician Education Program on Hospital Length of Stay and Total Patient Charges." *Journal of South Carolina Medical Association* 89(6):293-301, June 1993.

5. Mausner, J., and Kramer, S. *Mausner and Bahn Epidemiology.* Philadelphia, Pa.: W. B. Saunders, 1985.

6. Berwick, D. "The Clinical Process and the Quality Process." *Quality Management in Health Care* 1(1):1-8, Fall 1993.

7. Moore, C. "Using Experimental Design to Improve Clinical Processes." In *Quest for Quality and Productivity in Health Services* 1993 Conference Proceedings. Norcross, Ga.: Institute of Industrial Engineers, pp. 130-5.

8. Plackett, R., and Burman, J. "The Design of Optimum Multifactorial Experiments." *Biometrika* 33:305-25, 1946.

Suggested Readings

Box, G., and Bisgaard, S. "The Scientific Context of Quality Improvement." *Quality Progress* 20(6):54-61, June 1987.

Box, G., and others. *Statistics for Experimenters.* New York, N.Y.: John Wiley and Sons, 1978.

Box, J. R. A. Fisher: *The Life of a Scientist.* New York, N.Y.: John Wiley and Sons, 1978.

Cochran, W., and Cox, G. *Experimental Designs.* New York, N.Y.: John Wiley and Sons, 1950.

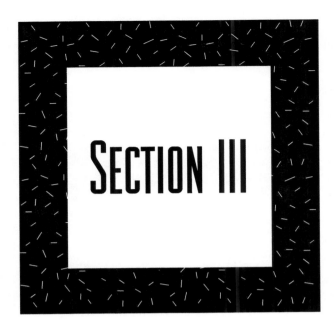

SECTION III

Topical Issues

The Toxicity of Pay for Performance*

by Donald M. Berwick, MD, MPP

She sat across the table from me, all ears—one of my very best employees. It was time for her annual merit review, and, according to the organization's policies, she was to be rated as "unsatisfactory," "satisfactory," "superior," or "outstanding," and receive a salary boost of zero, 4 percent, 5 percent, or 6 percent, respectively.

I had prepared carefully. Her work was promising indeed. Although she lacked formal training, she had clear leadership potential and enormous native talent for planning and organizing projects. To excel further, she would need to work on her writing and presentation skills, and some further study of simple statistical methods would strengthen her technical analyses. Tactfully, respectfully, pausing regularly for her questions, I explained my review, and offered her guidance. She asked no questions, but only nodded agreement with a friendly smile on her face. I ended with a review of my advice, and a handshake of congratulations for her fine efforts. I paused for her reflections.

"So," she asked, beaming—her first words since I had begun—"which is it...four percent, five percent, or six percent?"

It took me a few moments to absorb the full import of her question. But, finally, I saw the truth: she had not heard a word that I had said. "Four percent, five percent, or six percent?" That was her question, and that—and that alone—was what she was waiting to hear from me.

So embedded in our culture is the idea that "you get what you pay for," so familiar are the assumptions behind "pay for performance," so fair and obvious does it seem that people should be paid for their worth in American culture, that it may take a sledgehammer to ring a note of question. Indeed, in many corporate cultures, and most that I have worked in, to raise fundamental questions about these assumptions is inevitably to invite accusations of naivete and inexperience.

Linking pay to merit is an absolutely obvious instrument of proper management. Because it is absolutely obvious, it is difficult in the extreme to see that it is very nearly absolutely wrong. "Pay for performance" is as toxic to true organizational performance as any of the counterproductive tactics of outmoded, control-based management that enlightened organizations have long since, and much more readily, abandoned.

It is not necessary to recount here the classical arguments in favor of merit pay. They fall generally into two categories: arguments of *fairness* (good performance *deserves* its reward) and arguments of *incentive* (pay contingent on good performance generates more good performance).

In passing, we might note how thin is the empirical evidence for either of these arguments. There is little but logic or anecdote behind either assertion; in the entire volume of "classic" Harvard Business School papers assembled in a collection called, "Appraising Performance Appraisal," only a single experimental study appears.[1] But, as it happens, little real evidence can be found on either side of the "pay for performance" debate. (Alfie Kohn, a popular author on management systems of reward and incentive, claims that the evidence that does exist weighs heavily against contingent pay as a support for organizational or group effectiveness.[2]) Indeed, it is remarkable that an issue of such consequence for the guidance of organizations, and so hotly contested from time to time, has not benefitted more from proper social-scientific experimentation. We who debate pay for performance on either side must fall back on belief and logic for now for the bulk of our arguments.

Some clear definitions may help. Our topic here is "pay for performance," a contingent relationship, enforced and implemented in an organizational hierarchy, in which supervisors judge the merit of the work of those below them in the hierarchy and, based on those judgments, give out variable and contingent financial rewards. "Merit" can refer to meeting any goals or standards, whether negotiated in advance with the employee or announced arbitrarily, whether financial or nonfinancial, whether specific or ambiguous, whether quantitative or qualitative, whether measured in terms of throughput (e.g., "patients per day") or internal process (e.g., "reliable"). "Rewards" (and their opposite, "punishments") can be purely financial (such as salary increases or bonuses), or they may consist of other forms of organizational currency (such as promotion or perquisites). A key and essential component of "pay for performance" is the notion of *contingency*—the "merit" and the "reward" are linked explicitly, and the ultimate judge of both is the supervisor. Paying assembly-line workers on the basis of their productivity is "pay for performance"; so is paying individual doctors on the basis of their "clinical performance," however defined.

No dispute exists here about the value and appropriateness of dialogue between workers and supervisors about goals and performance. It is useful—indeed essential—in an effective organization that information flow freely about the extent to which needs are met, customers are satisfied, plans are implemented successfully, and goals are achieved. For many purposes, quantitative information is clearer and more instructive than mere narrative, and, accordingly, no dispute exists here about the great value of measuring performance in many dimensions and at many locations in the sequence of production.

Nor is there dispute here about the probability of and need for variation in compensation among individuals. There is a market for talents and experience, and an organization that tries to ignore the conclusions of that market will have trouble recruiting

Measuring Clinical Care: A Guide for Physician Executives

and retaining the people who can help it most. Changes in the cost of living, issues about the sharing of organizational profits, and employee demands that their compensation increase in accord with their skills will always be facts of organizational life, and compensation will therefore vary among people and over time.

No dispute exists here either about decisive remedial managerial action for either egregious misconduct or ineptitude, or, for that matter, about the festival celebration of real heroes. Those who cannot or should not do a job should leave that job—and be removed by the organization if they do not leave of their own accord; the occasional gold medalist deserves his or her medals and our applause.

But "pay for performance" goes beyond any of these. It is necessarily contingent and usually one-directional (top down), while dialogue about performance is not. It involves not variation in pay that is a fact of life enforced by the environment, but variation that senior leaders enforce by choice—and could change if they wished. It is a process applied not just to the occasional miscreant or the rare hero, but one maintained in the very fabric of the organization, affecting all by design.

Under this definition, "pay for performance" is guaranteed to be toxic in any organization in at least the following ways:

- **"Pay for performance" makes the supervisor the customer.** Organizations accountable to society or to markets must meet the needs of their customers in order to thrive. This is the central strategic message in modern quality management. Forget your customer, and, sooner or later, your customer will forget you. Modern management systems seek ways to help employees at all levels to inquire about external needs and demands and to take initiative to meet those needs. A "customer-focused" organization has inverted the pyramid of accountability; employees who meet and know the external customer are the *internal* customers of the management system. In such an organization, every supervisor needs to know how to improve his or her own ability to help others meet customers' needs.

  "Pay for performance" distorts this focus; it changes the direction of concern. Not necessarily in theory, but almost always in fact, the employee facing a supervisor about to dispense "four percent, five percent, or six percent" has one question foremost in mind—namely, "How can I please the supervisor?" This is, simply stated, *not* the key question upon which organizational survival depends. It diverts energy away from the true interests of the organization. The interests of the organization lie outside its walls; "pay for performance" turns people inward.

- **"Pay for performance" deprives the organization of essential information.** Because of this inversion of customer-supplier relationships within the organization, valuable information decays. Two losses are the most costly ones. First, supervisors learn less than they otherwise could about their own opportunities for improvement. Few employees facing merit reviews muster the courage to correct their supervisors, or to ask for better help in meeting customer needs. The person best able to help the supervisor gain knowledge about needed improvements in management is the employee, who is placed by "pay for performance" in the worst possible circumstance for giving that help.

Second, in the setting of performance review, the organization loses valuable information about defects. Suppose, for example, the supervisor credits the employee with a successful result on the basis of which the merit pay will increase, while the employee knows that the apparent "success" is not at all what it is being cracked up to be. What the organization needs is the information that the result was not good and that the information system is flawed; what the organization will probably get is a silent smile, warm thanks, and an employee now trapped between honesty and ingratitude.

- **"Pay for performance" increases internal competitiveness and barriers.** In the pursuit of quality, good fences make bad neighbors. A great organization today seeks constantly to cut windows among its functional areas and to help all employees feel more and more part of one team, with common pursuits and shared self-interest. "Pay for performance" never seems to hit this theme properly. Either the contingency is individualized, and people come to worry that they must cling to the credit so they will not lose the pay, or the contingency is set at such an extreme level of aggregation that the "congratulations for great performance" rings hollow to individuals, no one of whom ever can believe that he or she, alone, had much at all to do with the performance for which he or she is rewarded. The contingency upon which such variable pay is based tends therefore to be either fragmenting, at one extreme, or irrelevant, at the other. Either is damaging to relationships within the organization. If merit pay is individual, and especially if it is distributed down functional lines of hierarchy, employees will decrease the extent to which they share information and efforts across boundaries. One hospital CEO described to me his system of profit-center management, in which middle management bonuses depended on local budget performance. I asked him if one of his managers would transfer resources from his department to another's if it would help the organization as a whole. "Yes," the CEO answered honestly, "if he were crazy."

If merit pay appears in organizationwide bonuses, employees tend to feel helpless in responding to the contingency. I recall one hard day seeing patients at one stage in my professional life, a day that had been a constant uphill battle against missed appointments, unannounced patients with extremely complex problems, battles for approval with an outside utilization review office, and a frustrating search for speech therapy services for a mute three-year-old. The world seemed arrayed in opposition to my effectiveness, and I was exhausted as I began to open my mail late in the afternoon. Therein was a check for a "productivity bonus" of $297.00, and a note of organizational congratulations for my fine efforts—as it were, "Keep it up, fella." My first thought is not publishable. My second was, "Somebody doesn't understand at all."

- **"Pay for performance" costs a great deal to administer.** I know of no specific studies of the proportion of organizational energy that a "pay for performance" system consumes, but experience suggests that it is substantial. Elements of cost include the following: supervisory training; creating and managing forms and records; supervisory meetings and upward reporting; making decisions; justification, revision, grievance, and reply; administration of raises, bonuses, and rewards; goal-setting and goal-negotiation; and collecting and analyzing performance information. Greater still are

Measuring Clinical Care: A Guide for Physician Executives

the opportunity costs. Even at its best, "pay for performance" is still a system of "inspection" in a technical sense. Quality management theory counsels that the bulk of management energy should be devoted not to inspection of quality but to planning and improvement. Whatever time the management system is devoting to the inspection inherent in "pay for performance" is time denied to the much more significant management enterprise of quality planning and improvement.

Even if "pay for performance" produced benefit for the organization (and I dispute that conclusion), the benefit would have to be great enough to outweigh the high costs of maintaining the system.

■ **"Pay for performance" is inescapably unfair.** Statistical scions of quality management study the proportions of variation in quality and occurrence of defect that turn out empirically to be due to *people* in a system of production, compared with other causes in a system (such as the rules of procedure, the equipment, the raw materials, measurement error, and so on).[3] Even in service industries, and, to the extent it has been studied, even in health care, the preponderance of variation is not due to people but is due instead to other sources. (The relevant mental experiment would be to substitute a new workforce, randomly chosen from qualified candidates, in the current system, and then to ask if basic performance levels would change.)

At a deeper level, even the proportion of variation in performance that is attributable to "human" attributes of the system of production is, itself, complex in structure. A worker brings many attributes to the work: skills, knowledge, attitude, mood, experience, ethnicity, nonwork constraints, and ambitions, to name a few. A "pay for performance" system, especially if maintained for purposes of incentive, can reasonably attach contingent reward for individuals only to that portion of variable performance that is not only attributable to the individual but that is also, at least in principle, *under the control* of that individual. An "incentive" to make me a competitive downhill skier would have no chance of success; I have bad knees.

An all-knowing supervisor could adjust for this problem and make the contingencies apply only to the worker-controllable variation in performance. In practice, that is impossible. A back-of-the-envelope calculation shows the magnitude of the issue. Imagine, for argument's sake, that 30 percent of the variation in the productivity of physicians in an HMO is actually associated with individual characteristics (a proportion far greater than in most industries, and unlikely to be actually that high). Imagine, further, that half of that proportion is attributable to "controllable" characteristics (such as effort level and learnable skills), with the other half being associated with relatively immutable traits (such as the use of language, speed of calculation, and cautiousness in the face of risk). Thus, of variation in performance, 15 percent could be said to be susceptible to the motivation associated with merit pay and 85 percent not.

Now, imagine that a supervisor who observes variation in performance that is (in actual fact) *not* alterable by motivation reaches the correct conclusion (i.e., "incentives cannot help"), say, four out of five times. Imagine, also, that the same supervisor, when observing variation that *is* (in actual fact) alterable through motivation reaches the correct conclusion (i.e., "incentives can help") fully *half* the time. A simple calculation shows that, of all the instances in which the supervisor *thinks* that motivating the workers will produce better performance, fewer than one-third actually are of that type. (Here is the calculation: The supervisor attributes 0.2 x 85% = 17% of the observed variation to the worker when, in fact, the worker could not control the cause, and the supervisor attributes 0.5 x 15% = 7.5% of the observed variation correctly to the worker's motivation. Thus, when the supervisor says, "This was controllable by worker motivation, and I expect that incentives can help," the statement is correct only 7.5/(7.5 + 17) = 31% of the time.)

From the worker's point of view, this produces extraordinary irrationality in the reward structure. More than half the time that the supervisor "rewards" or "punishes" performance, for example, the worker is not in fact in control of that performance. The sense develops that the reward structure is blunt, arbitrary, and often unfair, because, statistically, it *is*, despite the best efforts of the supervisor to be fair. The unfairness comes from the statistical hazards of attributing cause in a complex causal system. Further, in the calculations used here for example, I presume that the discrimination abilities of the supervisor (80 percent "specificity" and 50 percent "sensitivity" for detecting variation that is reachable by incentives) are considerably better than I believe these abilities to be in most performance appraisal systems.

■ **"Pay for performance" reduces intrinsic motivation.** Many tasks, especially in health care, are potentially intrinsically satisfying. Relieving pain, answering questions, exercising manual dexterity, being confided in, working on a professional team, solving puzzles, and experiencing the role of a trusted authority—these are not at all bad ways to spend part of one's day at work. Pride and joy in the work of caring is among the many motivations that do result in "performance" among health care professionals.

In the rancorous debates about compensation, fees, and reimbursement that so occupy the time of health care leaders and clinicians today, it is all too easy to neglect, or even to doubt, that nonfinancial and intrinsic rewards are important in the work of medical care. Unfortunately, neglecting intrinsic satisfiers in work can inadvertently diminish them. Indeed, it has been possible in experimental settings to demonstrate a reduction in satisfaction from work by introducing extrinsic motivational factors. Students who will gladly work on a puzzle spontaneously when an experimental psychologist leaves them alone in a room will cease such spontaneous effort when the psychologist first offers to pay them to solve the puzzle.[4]

It is too much to say that pay for work does not support work, but it is psychologically tenable to assert that contingent pay for better work may decrease the joy one feels in that work. Deming called this phenomenon "overjustification" and believed that paying people to achieve what they would want to achieve anyway tends to reduce their satisfaction in the achievement.[5] My seven-year-old daughter read book after book, until her teacher began giving reading assignments and "stars" for completion, at which time completing reading "homework" became a nightly crisis.

Measuring Clinical Care: A Guide for Physician Executives

- "Pay for performance" slows change. Especially in health care, breakthroughs in performance will require substantial changes in the way we do our work. We require an unprecedented level of innovation if we are to produce better outcomes at substantially lower cost. Innovation does not come without risk.

Logically, I see no reason why contingent pay should decrease risk-taking; in theory, one ought to be able to rig it to support change. In actual practice, however, "pay for performance" seems almost always to exert a highly conservative, "anti-change" influence. When goals that will be the bases for variable compensation are set in advance, employees argue not for higher aspirations but for lower ones. The conversation about performance is a debate about what is possible, not about how to make something unprecedented possible. Long arguments take shape about how, exactly, performance will be measured—arguments that do not focus on the processes of work, but rather on the processes of *counting* work. Usually, failed experiments (the inevitable result of the willingness to take risk) result in deductions from "performance" scores, even if the risks were undertaken with the interests of the organization firmly in mind. Efforts in innovation, learning, and the satisfaction of curiosity—enormous assets in any organization that wants to accelerate improvement—are rarely counted as "performance," and even training and education, being nowhere reflected on the balance sheet, tend to be treated as "benefits" instead of as forms of "performance." Thus, "pay for performance," often introduced to assist an organization whose overall performance is unsatisfactory, tends to impede exactly those forms of systemic innovation and learning that are, in the long run, most likely to dig it out of trouble.

- **"Pay for performance" is disrespectful of human relationship.** In most adult social human interaction, contingency is rude. Who would accept a dinner invitation offered "in return for your good behavior"? We solve problems together in sports teams, families, clubs, and neighborhoods not by explicit, contingent economic exchange, but rather by building on our shared purposes, our common curiosity, our love, our sense of duty, or even by identifying the same enemy. "Pay for performance" is, with a few minor exceptions, generally reserved for only two settings: commercial contracts and work.

This segregation of work as *different* from other forms of human interaction is so common as to seem inescapable. But any student of the interior life of organizations knows that the social relationships—the noneconomic forces—endure nonetheless. Our employees help each other; affection develops and matures; teamwork counts on its own merits; people share their curiosity; and tribes emerge bound by common rituals and common enemies. When one looks closely, the contingent reward system—"pay for performance"—is as dissonant and distorting of the real life of the work setting as it would be at a dinner party. People hate it; it feels wrong; it has little to do with their valued relationships; it is an unwelcome game. Most of all, it erodes the potential for the true, interpersonal, adult-to-adult relationship of equals among all of the parties to organizational life. Fundamentally, as a human being, the CEO is not different in worth, character, or dignity from the lowest level employee.

In the final analysis, we either believe that, or we do not, and our actions reveal our beliefs far better than our words. Contingent pay down the line of hierarchy enforces the erosive fiction that we are not all of the same stuff.

This point echoes, of course, in religion, ethics, and values. But it echoes also in organizational performance. I cannot name a great team I have known in which an *internal* structure of contingent pay, doled out by one team member to another, seemed at the root of their greatness. Relationships mattered; purpose mattered; but "pay for performance" was not in the picture.

If "pay for performance" were not superficially logical, it would not have survived in the face of its obvious defects, and in the face of the dearth of good evidence to support it. It takes courage in organizations openly to doubt its worth, and even more courage to abandon it in favor of less well-described approaches to both pay and performance.

Defenders of merit pay will ask what the alternative is. There are no superb answers. Any viable system of compensation must respect market forces, employee demands for growth, and numerous other real-world factors. In addition, there are now strong pressures for various forms of gain-sharing, in which employees as a group benefit as stakeholders in overall organizational performance. Clever recognition and celebration systems, sometimes including financial reward, can apparently help support morale and energy for improvement. Some companies report success with "pay for learning" systems, in which growth in skills is recognized in the pay structure. These are all ideas worth developing further, but, for the present, the answers remain incomplete to the question: "If I do not pay people according to their performance, upon what other basis will I vary their pay?"

I find myself an extremist, and therefore suspicious of my answer. But it is, nonetheless, the best answer I have yet found regarding merit pay for doctors or any group of workers—namely, "Stop it." Merit pay, "pay for performance," and their close relatives are destructive of what we need most in our health care industry—teamwork, continuous improvement, innovation, learning, pride, joy, mutual respect, and a focus of all of our energies on meeting the needs of those who come to us for help. We can find better ways to decide on how we pay each other and better uses for our energies than in the study and management of carrots and sticks.

References

1. Harvard Business Review. *Appraising Performance Appraisal.* Boston, Mass.: Harvard Business School Press, 1993.

2. Kohn, A. "Why Incentive Plans Cannot Work." *Harvard Business Review* 71(5): 54-63, Sept.-Oct. 1993.

3. Scholtes, P. *An Elaboration on Deming's Teachings on Performance Appraisal.* Madison, Wis.: Joiner Associates, 1987.

4. Condry, J. "Enemies of Exploration: Self-Initiated Versus Other-Initiated Learning." *Journal of Personality and Social Psychology* 35(7):459-77, July 1977.

5. Deming, W. *The New Economics.* Cambridge, Mass.: Massachusetts Institute of Technology Press, 1993.

CHAPTER 15

Case for Linking Clinical Performance to Compensation

by Al M. Truscott, MD

The manner and the amount of their compensation invariably incite strong, emotional reactions in individuals and groups. For most people, the way they make their money and how much they get are ways of keeping score, not only economically but also in terms of self-worth and value to society. It can be argued that all compensation motivates, whether explicitly intended to or not. In other words, all compensation methods are linked to performance. In some instances, the link is to encourage certain types of behavior; in others, it is a reward after the behavior has occurred.

Organizations usually pay physicians in a planned, systematic manner. Often that system encourages certain behaviors. In many large group practices, compensation is based in part on "productivity," often defined as number of patients seen or procedures performed. Thus, physicians are rewarded for increasing the number of clinical events patients experience. Staff- and group-model HMOs and the military commonly pay physicians a salary, based primarily on tenure and specialty. Coupled with a set schedule of hours, this encourages the physician to ignore the time constraints within patient needs. In the university, individual compensation may in part depend on grant funds generated, encouraging attention to research projects. The recipient will view any system of payment as encouraging certain behaviors and discouraging others. It is impossible to have a value-free compensation system.

Complicating any discussion of compensation are the multiple ways in which an individual will feel rewarded, beyond dollars earned by salary. For example, a physician working in a single-specialty group will feel differently about his or her compensation depending on total take-home income; fringe benefits, such as pension plan; number of hours worked; number of nights of call; total patient load; and the quality of co-workers. The group can manipulate all of these factors, and some interact with others. Attempting to isolate any one of them as the prime motivation of physician behavior ignores their dynamic interaction.

Despite the complexity surrounding compensation as a motivation of behavior, many organizations nonetheless attempt to rationally design means to encourage certain behaviors and discourage others. And organizations that don't do this consciously are nonetheless motivating their physicians with whatever compensation system they use. The question is not *whether* to link performance to compensation (it always is) but *how*.

Models for Compensation Systems

Given a clean slate—say a start-up organization or a group of physicians who have agreed to design their compensation system from scratch—there are several steps one might ideally follow to determine how physicians will be paid. First, the mission and the values of the organization must be clearly defined, articulated, and understood by members of the group. The group must know why it exists, what service it intends to perform, and how it intends to do that. Specifically, the ways in which it receives revenue must be understood. If the money comes in on a capitated basis and is paid out on a per-service basis, there will be a mismatch between group goals and individual rewards.

Working from the mission and values of the organization, the group might then identify what general behaviors members expect of each other, such as how they will work together and how they will relate to patients. The characteristics desired of the physicians who will be part of the organization should be explicitly stated: Do we want physicians who will generate revenue for the organization, or do we want ones who will conserve the resources of the organization? Do we want ones who will take orders, or who will be able to act independently? This is a key step, because once the expected/desired behaviors are known, it is much easier to design a compensation system to reward for them.

Combining the mission and values of the organization with the desired behavior of physicians who work for that organization should help to define the compensation methodology chosen. There are a number of different methodologies currently in use, each with its own basis for determining income level. Most medical groups or organizations use one or a combination of them.

In a *marketplace-based* system, information is gathered about what one could earn in other locations for similar work. The theory is that there is a fluid labor market for physicians, who will naturally seek higher income, all other things being equal, as they look for places to establish practices. The reward inherent in this method is the opportunity cost of choosing one location over another.

A *productivity-based* system uses information about a physician's practice patterns to determine income. By producing more visits, procedures, hospital stays, or whatever is being counted, the physician can increase his or her compensation. This method is often chosen by organizations whose revenue comes on a per-service basis, in order to increase that revenue as much as possible.

Capitation is used more frequently by health maintenance organizations, either to individuals or to groups. This method is used for individuals primarily in independent practice associations, which compensate primary care providers a fixed amount per enrollee per month. Some HMOs contract with individual specialists on a capitated basis as well. These contracts may have performance clauses that compensate the physician on the basis of utilization of other health care services. Capitation theoretically encourages the use of only those services that are needed to diagnose and treat a patient's condition.

Measuring Clinical Care: A Guide for Physician Executives

Negotiation between an organization and an individual is sometimes used to determine income level. By definition, the criteria for payment will be unique in each case and are usually directly linked to a desire by the organization to meet the needs and interests of physicians.

Value-based compensation is not commonly used for the major portion of a physician's income. The value added to an organization by the physician's work is one way to use this method. Each organization will have a different definition of how value-added might be defined. For example, the value added to customers (patients and/or third-party payers) by a physician's services could be linked to the income received by that physician. Value to patients might be clinical outcomes; value to purchasers might be the cost of care.

By understanding what behaviors are desired from physicians, an organization or medical group can chose from among these various methods, or use some combination of them, to pay its physicians.

Linking Pay To Performance—Criteria for Success

Management theorists such as Alfie Kohn and W. Edwards Deming have argued against selectively rewarding workers in an organization. They posit that rewarding an individual for only certain aspects of his or her job performance will encourage neglect of other, equally important aspects of work. Individual incentive plans ignore the importance of teamwork and of the cooperation needed between various components of a work process. Incentive systems imposed by management are often not supple enough to reward for the specific performance needed in unique work areas. Especially for a profession such as medicine, which requires high degrees of independence and autonomy in action and decision making, coupled with extensive and continuing self-education, reward systems can inhibit the very behavior needed by patients receiving medical services. Multiple studies in management and social sciences have demonstrated that incentive programs rarely achieve their own stated goals of improved performance and productivity. In light of such information, is there any reason to consider linking a physician's performance to his or her pay?

I believe there is a reason, but it is not grounded in attempting to encourage by economic motivation certain behaviors from physicians. Most physicians prefer to be agnostic about the economic links between their clinical decisions and their income. This is demonstrated in our initial resistance to the word "customer" when used in place of "patient" in improvement theory. Customer refers to an exchange of money for a good or service; a customer is someone who is buying something, and we don't think we're selling anything. After some habituation, however, most physicians accommodate to the subtler qualities of meaning within the word "customer." This usually comes by recognizing that the approach to customers as taught by continuous improvement gurus is the same as the approach to patients presented by our most sensitive mentors in medical school.

Improvement theory, sometimes known as total quality management, starts with the premise that quality is defined by the customer, the person receiving the good or service. This is analogous to the physician starting with a patient's chief complaint. That complaint is further refined by questioning the patient and discovering as much information (through history, physical, and laboratory data) about that complaint as possible, finishing with designing an "improvement project" specific for that patient's complaint, testing the results, and refining the actions.

As physicians have learned more about improvement theory, they have discovered that successful organizations are those that learn what customers want and provide it to them—that is, they provide value to the customer. In health care, value can be defined as the sum of clinical health outcome (or status) and satisfaction with service divided by the cost of the service. In other words, our patients (and their third-party payers) are telling us they want excellent outcomes to their health problems, provided in a timely, caring, and thorough manner, at an affordable cost. What makes better sense than to link our compensation to meeting those expressed needs, those customer requirements?

In order to achieve that linkage, those being compensated should agree to it. Specific definitions of excellent clinical outcomes, superior service, and affordable cost must be developed, based on customer expectations, by those who are providing services, the physicians. This requires three steps: identifying the key outcomes, developing ways to measure them, and setting targets to be met. All of these actions are important irrespective of whether compensation is linked to performance, but agreement on which are the key clinical outcomes, and measuring them, seems to have eluded the medical profession up to this point. Linking physicians' economic success to their patients' success might accelerate the process.

It is not unusual to link compensation to the value received by the customer, but it is usually done on a collective, not an individual basis (one exception is the contingency fee system used by lawyers in liability cases; another is commissions earned on automobile and some retail sales). The price paid for most products and many services is linked in the customer's mind to the value received from that good or service. The availability of jobs, and the income received by the people producing the good or service, thus depend on their ability to generate that value.

Most arguments against paying for performance focus on plans that link individual behavior to income received. As improvement theory teaches, customer requirements are best met by empowered teams working with well-designed processes and systems. A part of that empowerment can mean turning a work group from a cost center into a revenue or profit center. That simple act fundamentally links compensation—broadly defined as above—to group performance.

Summary

All compensation methods inherently link performance to reward. Compensation must be thought of as including not only income received but also hours worked, number of co-workers, amount of work expected, and quality of work environment. Value-added compensation systems consider what the customer is willing to pay for the relative quality of product or service received. Improvement theory identifies the importance of customer requirements in defining value and of empowered teams supplying it. Having clearly defined outcome and process measurements based on customer requirements linked to some part of group compensation is one way to ensure that the medical group's success will reflect its patients' success.

CHAPTER 16

An Argument for Linking Compensation to Performance

by Steven L. Zatz, MD, and Cary Sennett, MD, PhD

The question of whether to link performance to compensation is in some sense moot; the horse has long since left the barn. Under traditional arrangements, doctors are paid for doing things (and not paid for not doing things). Thus, fee-for-service medicine has always linked performance to compensation, albeit in a manner that we believe leaves much to be desired.

One of the common features of managed care is to implement alternatives to fee-for-service payment for providers who control or influence the consumption of resources. A range of compensation arrangements, including capitation and per case payment, serve the objective of shifting a certain amount of risk and responsibility to providers of care. However, such systems have the potential to reward doctors who provide less care. Those who perform fewer services may be able to care for (and be compensated for) additional patients and/or enjoy more leisure time. Once again, compensation is linked to performance, but now in a manner opposite to that of the traditional fee-for-service system.

So the real topic for discussion is not whether compensation should be linked to performance, because, across America and across practice settings, it already is. Compensation is not, however, linked to the quality of the performance—the outcomes achieved by virtue of the selection of services and the nature of their application. And so the real issue is: Should the quality of a physician's performance be linked to his or her compensation? And if it should, what sort of linkage makes the most sense?

At the outset, we submit that the linkage implicit in the current practice of fee-for-service medicine is flawed; compensating physicians simply for doing *more* makes no sense when what we want to do is compensate them for doing *better*. As a result, we are not sanguine about the possibility that any compensation system that is fundamentally based on fee-for-service can motivate the delivery of high-quality—and continuously improving—health care. We begin our consideration of the linkage of performance and compensation from the perspective that a better foundation for payment can be constructed from systems, such as capitation, that shift some responsibility to the providers of care.

An Instructive Example

Imagine that you are a primary care doctor and that you participate in a managed health care plan that uses capitation to compensate you for the care that you provide to your panel of patients. Your practice can be characterized as follows: To the extent that they exist, you follow evidence-based guidelines that have received endorsement from nationally respected organizations and societies. You have organized your office so that you can provide extended hours to patients who work or otherwise find it difficult to get to your office during regular working hours. You make it a point to study and incorporate into your practice information gleaned from continuing medical education courses and careful reading of the medical literature. Your patients are surveyed concerning the extent to which the care that you provide meets their expectations, and they are generally very satisfied with all aspects of the care that you provide to them. You make every effort to reach out to your panel of patients and alert them to the need for a range of preventive services, such as immunizations, Pap smears, and mammographic screening. When your patients are admitted to hospitals, you continue to manage their care and actively support efforts to arrange for the out-of-hospital services that reduce the length and the cost of their hospital stays. You are working as hard as you can to provide high-quality, cost-effective care to health plan members who have chosen you as their primary care doctor, and there is objective evidence of a high level of achievement and improvement over time.

Now consider another doctor who participates in the same health care plan. His office closes early and offers no night or weekend hours. He decries all guidelines as "cookbook medicine." He completes the minimum number of continuing medical education credits required by the state licensing board and makes no effort to translate new knowledge into changes in practice. He does not believe that patients can assess any aspect of the care they receive and does not understand why a doctor would pay attention to survey responses. He provides Pap tests and immunizations to patients who make appointments for them but otherwise makes no effort to bring his panel of patients into compliance with current recommendations for preventive care. Perhaps because there are relatively few primary care physicians in the area in which you live, both you and your counterpart have full practices. The turnover rate among your colleague's patients, however, is much higher than among your panel of patients.

Now consider this: Both you and your counterpart receive the same compensation from the health care plan. In fact, your colleague (whose practice costs are lower) nets more than you do! Does this make sense? We think not. We believe strongly that the manner of provider payment should encourage and reward better care. And so the question is: What are the features of a performance-based compensation system that increase the likelihood that consumers receive high-quality, cost-effective health care that improves over time?

Design of a Performance-Based Compensation System

As with most things in life, the compensation of doctors and other health care professionals need not be driven by esoteric theory but, instead, can be informed principally by common sense. Ideally, payment in health care should depend, at least in part, on the short- and long-term effect of the care provided on patients' health and well-being, as well as on the responsible use of resources in the pursuit of desired outcomes. Customers for health care services should be the ones to determine the quality of the care provided. However, health care presents particular challenges with regard to the customer's evaluation of performance, including:

■ The circumstance that the principal customer, the patient, often does not bear directly the full costs of the services provided, which results in other interested parties that may not have the same perspective as the patient.

■ Limitations in the ability of all the various customers for health care services to evaluate directly the quality and efficiency of the care provided. While the patient's inability to evaluate his or her care is often overstated, it is true that aspects of the medical services provided to patients may be more difficult for the consumer to judge than those services provided by, for instance, car rental agencies or fast food establishments.

When a managed care organization constructs a performance-based provider compensation system, it must do so as the agent for its members and the entities that purchase their health care benefits. To the extent that the managed care organization wishes to meet the needs of its customers, it will solicit their input in the design and ongoing operation of its programs.

The unique aspects of health care notwithstanding, the critical elements of a performance-based compensation system include:

■ Identification of desired results and the factors that lead to desired results.

■ Development of performance measures and measurement systems pertaining to desired results.

■ Specification of the relationship between performance and compensation.

In addition, an organization must have processes in place to address the need to continuously improve its methods of assessment and compensation.

Identifying Desired Results

The meaning and purpose of health care encounters involves a complex set of issues that cannot be explored fully in the context of the present discussion. Nevertheless, we believe there is general consensus that health care services are desirable to the extent that they:

■ Improve clinical status (e.g., reduce blood pressure, improve diabetes control, lead to the discovery of illness at the most treatable stage).

■ Improve functional status (e.g., improve physical functioning, reduce level of pain).

■ Provide satisfaction to patients (e.g., meet patient expectations).

■ Do all of this at the lowest possible cost.

The objectives of a performance-based compensation strategy must be to encourage health care providers and systems to act in a manner that increases the likelihood of achieving these desirable results.

Developing Measures to Assess Performance

A number of different frameworks may be helpful for constructing measures of the performance of health care providers. Since Donabedian, the triad of structure, process, and outcome has frequently been employed as a foundation for discussions of quality of care.[1] A related framework, which we have found to be useful, includes:

- Access to care—availability of doctors and other health care providers, facilities, and services necessary to meet the various health care needs of an identified population.

- Capability to provide care—degree to which a health care provider's formal training and practical experience support the delivery of care and the achievement of desired outcomes.

- Aspects of technical performance—attributes of tests and procedures, such as the accuracy and completeness of diagnostic imaging studies, that maximize the likelihood of successful diagnosis and treatment.

- Aspects of cognitive performance—cognitive activities that are not direct decisions about patient management (but that influence them), for example, the correctness of the interpretation of imaging studies and laboratory tests.

- Appropriateness of care—correctness of decisions concerning the diagnosis and treatment of patients in relationship to the recommendations in well-constructed, evidence-based, practice policies.

- Patient satisfaction with care—patients' perceptions of their experiences with the health care system in the context of their expectations.

- Outcomes of care—direct and proxy measures for the current and future health status and well-being of patients.

- Costs of care—direct (consumed in the context of patient care) and indirect (e.g., lost productivity of workers, lost school days) costs related to health care.

This broad range of measurement implies identification of a variety of data sources and creation of systems to store and analyze performance information. There is much relevant information in data already collected and maintained for purposes other than performance measurement by organizations such as hospitals and managed care companies. Sources for performance-related information include professional claims and encounters, pharmacy claims, laboratory results, and patient and health provider survey responses. We believe that there will be a rapid growth in databases that combine administrative data with selected clinical information and survey responses for the purpose of supporting efforts to assess and improve the delivery of health care services.

Measuring Clinical Care: A Guide for Physician Executives

The Relationship between Performance and Compensation

There is no simple formula to relate level of performance to level of compensation. Some general principles, however, are clear:

■ Compensation should rise as objective performance improves. Physicians whose performance is better should receive proportionately higher rates of compensation, and physicians whose performance improves over time should observe their compensation rise as well.

■ A nontrivial portion of total compensation should be linked to performance. There is not a single formula for performance-based compensation that will apply to all organizations; each entity must devise a system that is compatible with its culture, goals, and measurement capabilities.

■ Performance-based compensation cannot be used in isolation as a means to improve care and outcomes. Where there is commitment to improving quality, there must be a set of related initiatives, all of which operate to move the delivery system in the optimal direction. Compensation is only one element in that set. It is the full commitment of the health plan (and the complete set of collaborative activities that the commitment engenders) that is the key to performance improvement.

Concerns Associated with Performance-Based Compensation

Are there potential problems with performance-based compensation? Of course, but none that cannot be managed. For example, there is legitimate concern that a theoretically sound strategy for linking performance to compensation will have undesired effects, because measurement systems are currently incapable of evaluating performance reliably. There has been particular concern about issues of risk adjustment (see Chapter 10): If "better" physicians attract more severely ill patients, their outcomes may appear to be worse than those of their less proficient colleagues. Failure to properly adjust for differences in risk and severity may lead to conclusions about physician performance that are incorrect. The problem is compounded by the lack of any "gold standard" methodology against which to compare a particular approach to performance evaluation.

There is no doubt that additional research is required in areas of health care performance assessment. However, sufficient measures exist to support performance measurement in a number of areas, and promising new technology is under development at a number of academic and private-sector research centers. One needs to be careful not to let the perfect be the enemy of the good here; experience with available measurement tools suggests that, employed judiciously, they can be implemented successfully and can have a positive impact on health system performance. For over six years now, U.S. Healthcare has linked a portion of primary care physicians' compensation to their performance on measures that include patient ratings of care and compliance with practice policies pertaining to preventive services, such as immunizations and cholesterol screening.[2] While no formal studies have been initiated to determine the relative influence of feedback of performance information versus feedback plus financial incentives, we believe that improvements in performance that have been observed on measures contained in the compensation model are due, in part, to a system that provides monetary rewards for better performance.

As with any system of evaluation, there are concerns that those being evaluated may focus on the items being measured at the expense of other aspects of performance that are also important. Health care involves a complex set of inputs and outputs, and it is not possible to measure them all accurately and economically at the present time. As a result, an organization needs to seek broad input into its construction and weighting of a set of measures intended to be representative of a particular category of services (e.g., primary care, obstetrical care) provided to patients. As better data capture occurs in medicine, it should be easier to measure a range of services and their outcomes without resorting to extensive chart review and other expensive means of data collection.

Performance-Based Compensation: Reality versus Theory

Some have argued that it is inappropriate to use compensation as a means to motivate improved performance in any field of endeavor. With regard to medicine in particular, some have argued that, because physicians are inherently motivated to provide high-quality care, the introduction of performance incentives is an example of tampering with a system that works. We disagree. While we fully understand that health care professionals are motivated by many factors other than compensation—including recognition by patients, peers, and the community; altruism; and fear of litigation—there is convincing evidence that the method of payment also influences physician behavior.[3-8] To the extent that compensation is a motivating force, we believe that it is not only legitimate but, in fact, required that those who are charged by their customers with the management of health care resources and outcomes use every means available to them to do so.

An environment in which health care providers are rewarded on the basis of the excellence of their performance should lead to better patient outcomes and more appropriate levels of health care spending. Such an environment is an essential component of successful reform of our health care system. We envision a health care marketplace in which information is available to consumers wishing to make rational health care decisions and to health care providers seeking to improve their performance. We see greater use of performance-based compensation as an important component of an increasingly competitive health care system characterized by continuous improvement in the efficiency and effectiveness of the services provided to its customers.

References

1. Donabedian, A. *The Definition of Quality and Approaches to Its Assessment.* Ann Arbor, Mich.: Health Administration Press, 1980.

2. Schlackman, N. "Evolution of a Quality-Based Compensation Model: The Third Generation." *American Journal of Medical Quality* 8(2):103-10, Summer 1993.

3. Hillman, A., and others. "How Do Financial Incentives Affect Physicians' Clinical Decisions and the Financial Performance of Health Maintenance Organizations?" *New England Journal of Medicine* 321(2):86-92, July 13, 1989.

4. Hemenway, D., and others. "Physicians' Responses to Financial Incentives. Evidence from a For-Profit Ambulatory Care Center." *New England Journal of Medicine* 322(15):1059-63, April 12, 1990.

5. Krasnik, A., and others. "Changing Remuneration Systems: Effects on Activity in General Practice." *British Medical Journal* 300(6741):1698-701, June 30, 1990.

6. Hillman, B., and others. "Frequency and Costs of Diagnostic Imaging in Office Practice—A Comparison of Self-Referring and Radiologist-Referring Physicians." *New England Journal of Medicine* 323(23):1604-8, Dec. 6, 1990.

7. Stearns, S., and others. "Physician Responses to Fee-for-Service and Capitation Payment." *Inquiry* 29(4):416-25, Winter 1992.

8. Murray, J., and others. "Ambulatory Testing for Capitation and Fee-for-Service Patients in the Same Practice Setting: Relationship to Outcomes." *Medical Care* 30(3):252-61, March 1992.

CHAPTER 17

Clinical Guidelines: A Tool for Quality Improvement

by David N. Sundwall, MD

Current interest in developing clinical guidelines can be traced to research studies published in the 1970s and early 1980s that documented surprising variations in clinical practices[1] and a growing body of evidence that much health care is unnecessary, inappropriate, and potentially harmful.[2] As this research became more widely known and was presented to policymakers struggling with how to control ever escalating health care expenditures, questions about the appropriateness and value of costly medical services gained national attention.

In 1988, Arnold Relman, MD, then editor of the *New England Journal of Medicine*, declared that the United States was on the brink of a "third revolution in medicine," the *Era of Assessment and Accountability*.[3] He characterized the previous two eras as the *Era of Expansion* (1940s-1960s) and the *Era of Cost Containment* (1970s-1980s). A revolution leading to the third era in the 1980s was taking place because multiple efforts to contain health care costs over the previous two decades, in both private and public sectors, had failed, Relman said. He wrote about a growing sense that it would be impossible to restrain health care spending with the "ever increasing volume and intensity of medical services being provided in outpatient settings and hospitals."[3]

In addition, Relman said, third-party payers were frustrated by the unknown quality and outcomes of care provided, as well as the discovery of large geographical variations in costs and the frequency with which various services were provided without discernible differences in outcomes. Thus, a strong consensus was developing that improved bases were needed for making medical decisions—diagnostic and therapeutic—and for deciding when and when not to intervene. In short, there was growing recognition of a need for uniformity in how and when care is provided—that is, for *clinical guidelines*—and for ways to determine if the care provided actually makes a positive difference in the lives of patients, that is, through measurement of *health outcomes*.

Evidence that the United States has entered this new era of assessment and accountability is provided by two significant developments in federal health policy that occurred in the late 1980s:

- The Health Care Financing Administration (HCFA) released Medicare data to the public for the purpose of research in the private sector related to medical effectiveness and medical appropriateness.

- A new entity, the Agency for Health Care Policy and Research (AHCPR), was established in the Public Health Service. AHCPR's primary mission, according to its first administrator, Jarrett Clinton, MD, is to "find out what works and what doesn't" in medical care.

The first of these actions, taken by HCFA's Administrator at the time, William Roper, MD, was intended to make health-related HCFA information files available for use in assessing the appropriateness and effectiveness of various procedures and interventions.[4] The establishment of AHCPR was required by Congress as part of the Omnibus and Reconciliation Act of 1989 (OBRA'89), bringing what many believed was long overdue attention to health services research and health care technology assessment. But AHCPR was not created merely to promote health services research; it was specifically charged with developing, in collaboration with the private sector, "clinically relevant guidelines." Furthermore, AHCPR was given the responsibility to make such guidelines widely available to providers and consumers (patients) to facilitate better-informed and more rational medical care choices and decisions.

Such high-level attention to health services research, the effectiveness of clinical care, and specifically the development of clinical practice guidelines has been enthusiastically welcomed by many—the academic community, third-party payers, and those involved in health policy. However, scrutiny of clinical care, particularly under government auspices, has been less well received by many clinicians and has been viewed skeptically by some as just another in a series of well-intentioned efforts ostensibly focused on quality improvement but, in fact, motivated by cost containment.[5] Such skepticism notwithstanding, federal efforts have catalyzed a remarkable increase in interest and activity in clinical guideline development.

To be sure, similar efforts have been undertaken for years by professional organizations, medical specialty societies, hospital-based quality improvement teams, and others. The scope of such activity is documented by the American Medical Association's (AMA's) Office of Quality Assurance and Healthcare Organizations. That office publishes annually, and updates quarterly, a *Directory of Practice Parameters* (its preferred term for clinical guidelines), which offers a range of appropriate strategies for the management of specific clinical conditions. The 1994 edition lists approximately 1,600 parameters.[6]

Who Uses Guidelines?
It seems that a majority of individuals concerned about American health care policies and issues are looking to clinical guidelines to provide better outcomes, that is, to improve the chances for obtaining the intended results of medical care. It is generally assumed that quality of care can be improved by employing clinical guidelines and, thus, that those involved in providing clinical care and conducting quality assessment, measurement, and monitoring of such care can be expected to embrace this approach. Recent examples of guidelines developed in the private sector and sponsored by the government include:

Measuring Clinical Care: A Guide for Physician Executives

- *Practice Guidelines for the Administration of Fresh Frozen Plasma, Cryoprecipitate, and Platelets,* published by the development Task Force of the College of American Pathologists.[7]

- *Clinical Practice Guidelines Number 14: Acute Low Back Problems in Adults,* published by AHCPR, December 1994; *Number 15; Treatment of Pressure Ulcers,* December 1994; and *Number 16; Post Stroke Rehabilitation* May 1995.[8]

Other activities illustrate how broadly clinical guidelines are now being applied.

Illinois Blue Cross and Blue Shield (BC/BS) is including conformance to clinical practice guidelines as a condition of participation in contracts offered to some specialists who are applying to join a new BC/BS point-of-service network. Eight guidelines have been developed, and more are on the way. In spite of objections from medical organizations, the President of Illinois BC/BS, Arnold Widen, MD, states that its customers are excited because the guideline program provides tangible evidence of BC/BS commitment to maintaining quality.[9]

The New York State Department of Health Cardiac Surgery Reporting System, begun in 1988, has published four-year statewide and hospital-specific outcomes, resulting in the development of clinical guidelines for cardiac bypass surgery.[10]

The use of clinical guidelines as a basis for legal defense against malpractice is currently being tested in Maine. The five-year demonstration project is intended to determine the validity of guidelines in four clinical areas—obstetrics and gynecology, radiology, emergency medicine, and anesthesiology.

Apparently, then, there is widespread enthusiasm for using clinical guidelines for a variety of purposes ranging well beyond traditional measurement of the quality of clinical care.

Appropriate Use of Guidelines

Despite all the interest in guidelines, there is scant documentation of how they are being used. To date, far more effort has been put into developing guidelines than into promoting their use and ascertaining if, in fact, they are being used as intended. Outcomes of care cannot be judged as good or bad, or as resulting from the provider's following or failing to follow clinical guidelines, unless we know if, and how, such guidelines have been applied. In short, just because a large variety of guidelines have been developed does not mean that they are being used effectively.

That guidelines should be applied appropriately, however, is fundamental to the success of the guideline movement in facilitating better outcomes of clinical care, a concern that did not escape the attention of those who drafted legislation to authorize the AHCPR. In addition to charging the new federal agency with responsibility for promoting the development of clinical guidelines, the law also directed the AHCPR to develop "standards of quality, performance measures, and medical review criteria through which health care providers and other appropriate entities may assess or review the provision of health care and assure its quality."[11]

To help fulfill this legislative mandate, AHCPR convened a work group in 1992 consisting of 18 health professionals, health information specialists, lawyers, payers, regulators, and researchers. Consultants and technical experts were also included. Over a two-year period, they worked to develop a report titled, "Using Clinical Practice Guidelines to Evaluate Quality of Care: Issues and Methods." This document was recently published in two volumes—#1, Issues, and #2, Methods—and can be obtained from AHCPR.[12]

One of the work group's strategies was to review existing methods for translating clinical guidelines into quality measures. It found that there were no such documented or widely used evaluation instruments. Consequently, it determined to develop translation methodologies, believing that tools for evaluating the quality of care could be potentially useful to a wide variety of users. In fact, the development of valid guideline-derived quality measures was considered an essential step in the transformation of medicine from a craft, passed on largely through apprenticeship, into an enterprise based on facts about the relationship between processes and outcomes of care.

The following recommendations are derived from the efforts of the AHCPR work group. They represent only a conceptual framework of guideline-derived quality measurement. Dr. R. Heather Palmer and Naomi Banks of the Harvard School of Public Health deserve much of the credit for the specific recommended methodology. Their work is included in the AHCPR document.

Using Clinical Guidelines to Measure Quality of Care

Scientifically sound practice guidelines, if followed as intended, can contribute to improved patient care outcomes—for example, decreased morbidity, decreased mortality, shorter lengths of stay in hospitals, and improved functional status. For the most part, however, clinical guidelines specify the *processes* of care, and, consequently, determining quality of care based on such guidelines is a measurement of process.

To illustrate, consider the so-called Quality Management Cycle, or the Shewart Cycle (figure 1, page 153). In its simplest form, this cycle consists of *planning* a new or improved process (for example a clinical practice guideline), *doing* or implementing the process (conducting a particular medical intervention according to the specifications of the guideline), *checking* or measuring to see if the process is working as planned to improve outcomes, and then *acting* upon the information to reassess the plan (guideline) or continue its implementation.

As we have indicated, there seems to have been far more planning or development of clinical guidelines to date than doing, checking, or acting on the results of their use. The following recommendations relate to checking or measuring, the third step in the Quality Management Cycle. They can help us determine if a particular guideline has been used as intended and if it resulted in the anticipated outcome.

Definitions

Perhaps the first hurdle to overcome is agreeing on common terminology. The work group adapted definitions, indicated in table 1, page 153, from the Institute of Medicine's Committee on Clinical Practice Guidelines.

Measuring Clinical Care: A Guide for Physician Executives

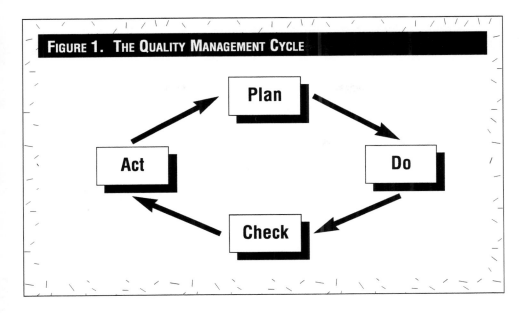

FIGURE 1. THE QUALITY MANAGEMENT CYCLE

Plan → Do → Check → Act → (Plan)

TABLE 1. DEFINITIONS

Clinical Practice Guidelines
Systematically developed statements to assist practitioners' and patients' decisions about health care to be provided for specific clinical circumstances.

Medical Review Criteria
Systematically developed statements that can be used to assess specific health care decisions, services, and outcomes.

Performance Measures
Methods or instruments to estimate or monitor the extent to which the actions of a health care practitioner or provider conform to the clinical practice guideline.

Standards of Quality
Authoritative statements of (1) minimum levels of acceptable performance or results, (2) excellent levels of performance or results, or (3) the range of acceptable performance or results.

Source: Adapted from Institute of Medicine, Committee on Clinical Practice Guidelines. *Clinical Practice Guidelines; Directions for a New Program.* Field, M., and Lohr, K., Eds. Washington, DC: National Academy Press, 1990.

Medical review criteria and *performance measures* are used to determine the degree to which care has followed specific processes. When *standards of quality* are applied to the measurement, one can determine whether the care provided met predetermined goals or targets for performance. The relationship between clinical practice guidelines, medical review criteria, performance measures, and standards of quality is shown in figure 2, below.

Example of Guideline-Derived Evaluation Instruments
The following discussion illustrates how to develop evaluation instruments—medical review criteria, performance measures, and standards of quality—from a specific clinical practice guideline, in this case AHCPR's guideline on acute pain management.

One of the specific recommendations is that "pain should be assessed and documented routinely at regular intervals postoperatively, as determined by the operation and the severity of pain" (for example, every two hours while the patient is awake for one day after surgery).

Referring to the definition of *medical review criteria*, it is clear that the first step in the process is to derive a statement from the guideline that can be used to assess whether or not the recommended health care decisions or services were carried out. Thus, for this particular recommendation, a medical review criterion was determined as follows: "For the patient recovering from surgery, the patient's pain was assessed and documented every two hours while awake for the first 24 hours." Note that the *guideline* recommends what should be done for the patient before care was provided; the *medical review criterion* attempts to document what was done after care was provided.

This particular aspect of a patient's care may be applied to judge the performance of an individual provider on a case-by-case basis. However, the information could also be

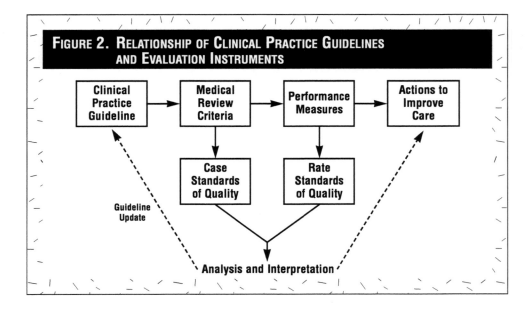

FIGURE 2. RELATIONSHIP OF CLINICAL PRACTICE GUIDELINES AND EVALUATION INSTRUMENTS

Measuring Clinical Care: A Guide for Physician Executives

TABLE 2. EXAMPLE OF CLINICAL PRACTICE GUIDELINE-DERIVED EVALUATION INSTRUMENTS FOR DETERMINING THE QUALITY OF CARE FOR POSTOPERATIVE PAIN CONTROL

Clinical Practice Guideline Recommendation

Pain should be assessed and documented routinely at regular intervals postoperatively, as determined by the operation and the severity of pain (e.g., every two hours while awake for 1 day after surgery).

Medical Review Criterion

For the patient recovering from surgery, pain was assessed and documented every two hours while awake for the first 24 hours following surgery.

Performance Measure

Calculate the following for consecutive surgical patients seen over a six-month period: the number of patients whose pain was assessed and documented every two hours while awake. The performance measure = $\frac{\text{\# meeting criterion}}{\text{\# of surgery patients}}$ x 100 percent

Standard of Quality

A performance rate of 95 percent or less triggers a review to determine how to improve assessing and documenting the patient's pain status every two hours while awake for the first 24 postoperative hours.

used to develop a measure of a provider's performance over time for a number of patients (*performance measure*). This is done by dividing the number of patients cared for over time whose care met the criterion specified by the total number of postoperative patients the provider was responsible for.

A third evaluation instrument is standards of quality. Such standards are determined by the institution or organization and indicate a range of acceptable performance. For example, an organization might decide that anything less than 95 percent conformance to the recommended frequency of checking for patient's pain every two hours would lead to a review of the provider's effectiveness. These steps are illustrated in table 2, above.

Steps Required

The task—to develop medical review criteria for several specific recommendations of each clinical guideline—may seem overwhelming. However, no matter what type of review is undertaken, it can be accomplished if certain steps are followed. At a minimum, the steps in table 3, page 156, are recommended. While this may seem like a lot of work, it can be greatly aided by the use of algorithms and by computerization of the process. Figure 3, page 157, illustrates an algorithm for a medical review criterion for the AHCPR's cataract guideline.

Clinical Guidelines: A Tool for Quality Improvement   155

TABLE 3.	STEPS RECOMMENDED TO DEVELOP AND IMPLEMENT GUIDELINE-DERIVED PERFORMANCE MEASURES

■ Identify a relevant clinical practice guideline.

■ Select guideline recommendations you wish to monitor, and draft the appropriate medical review criteria.

■ Identify clinicians using this guideline and sites of care.

■ Determine a patient sample to monitor.

■ Identify sources of data (e.g., nursing records, outpatient chart, etc.).

■ Write medical review criteria.

■ Specify data items needed and forms required for documentation.

■ Conduct review—assign criteria status.

■ Report review findings.

■ Interpret findings, apply standards of quality (as determined appropriate by the institution or organization conducting the review).

■ Act on review findings.

Preliminary Considerations

The steps required to develop evaluation instruments derived from clinical practice guidelines to assess quality of care seem clear enough; however, as with most aspects of patient care, the steps are, in fact, not easy and require a commitment of resources and personnel. While the recommended methodology is conceptually straightforward, several matters should be considered before beginning.

Implicit vs. Explicit Review

Perhaps the most important consideration is that, traditionally, quality assurance has been conducted on a case-by-case basis by "peers," that is, by trusted physicians reviewing the charts of their colleagues. Judgments have been based on personal experience of what was acceptable or not. This is called *implicit review*. However, implicit review judgments have been shown to vary greatly, principally because the reason for making

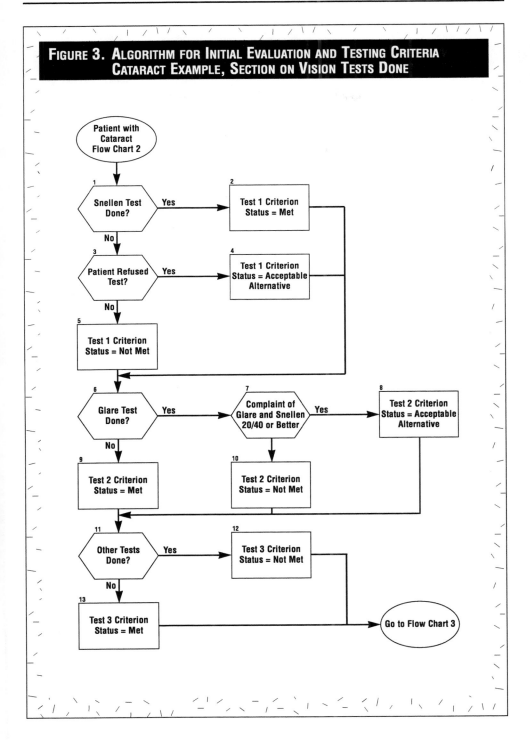

FIGURE 3. ALGORITHM FOR INITIAL EVALUATION AND TESTING CRITERIA CATARACT EXAMPLE, SECTION ON VISION TESTS DONE

Patient with Cataract Flow Chart 2

1 Snellen Test Done? — Yes → 2 Test 1 Criterion Status = Met

No ↓

3 Patient Refused Test? — Yes → 4 Test 1 Criterion Status = Acceptable Alternative

No ↓

5 Test 1 Criterion Status = Not Met

6 Glare Test Done? — Yes → 7 Complaint of Glare and Snellen 20/40 or Better — Yes → 8 Test 2 Criterion Status = Acceptable Alternative

No ↓

9 Test 2 Criterion Status = Met

10 Test 2 Criterion Status = Not Met

11 Other Tests Done? — Yes → 12 Test 3 Criterion Status = Not Met

No ↓

13 Test 3 Criterion Status = Met

Go to Flow Chart 3

determinations of what is "good or bad," acceptable or not, remain largely a matter of opinion in the mind of the reviewer.

To improve the validity of case review and reduce costs by conserving the reviewer's time, efforts have been made over the past decade to have clinicians write down the criteria to be used in judging quality. These criteria could then be applied by nonclinicians to case reviews, thus screening out only those that did not meet specific criteria. This is called *explicit review*. Although it is more time-consuming and resource intensive, such an approach is without question more reliable and valid. In fact, both the Institute of Medicine and AHCPR promote such explicit review. The methodology recommended for translating clinical practice guidelines into quality measurement tools depends on such explicit review.

Other Issues

The following issues are relevant to quality measurement based on clinical practice guidelines (for a detailed discussion, consult reference 12):

■ **Who should participate**

Ideally, a defined multidisciplinary group, including clinicians, quality management professionals, and health information management personnel, would be committed to such a project over time. When possible, researchers and statisticians should be involved.

■ **Variation in resources**

There is great variation in the resources—human, financial, material (e.g., data and computers)—available to those interested in conducting quality assessment. For example, a small rural hospital may have only a few individuals involved in such activities and only limited access to information technologies. However, the fundamental steps recommended here can still be taken, beginning with clinical problems considered most likely to enhance patient care in the institution involved. Where skills and resources are not directly available, they may be obtained through consultation or participation in a consortium.

■ **Training and education**

Proper orientation is vital to success in developing and applying guideline-derived evaluation instruments. Those involved need to understand the process and become familiar with data and statistical tools necessary to develop performance measures over time, (i.e., document trends and variance). The extent to which involved individuals are comfortable with the terminology and process will determine their commitment over time.

■ **Variation in process**

To date, how evaluation instruments are developed varies greatly, mainly because a generic methodology has never been developed to guide the process. Multiple methods are not necessary, desirable, or needed, however. In order to be based on guidelines, true comparability of outcomes information must be obtained by rigorous application of evaluation instruments derived according to a replicable method, as described here, whether for determining quality of care, for reimbursement purposes, or as a legal defense.

Summary

For the past decade, enthusiasm has grown among many professional and lay groups for the development and various applications of clinical practice guidelines. Regardless of who is using such guidelines, or for what purposes, it is critical that health professionals understand how to gain the maximum benefit from using these clinical tools. In order for any judgment to be made about health care delivered according to recommendations based on clinical practice guidelines, such care must be evaluated with instruments that have been developed according to rigorous methodology. While the process may not be easy, it will be worth the effort invested. Using evaluation instruments to judge the effectiveness of clinical guidelines will contribute to the science of quality assessment and should be welcomed by those whose clinical decisions and care are being evaluated.

References

1. Wennberg, J. "Dealing with Medical Practice Variations: A Proposal for Action." *Health Affairs* 3(2):6-32, Summer 1984.

2. Brook, R. "Quality of Care: Do We Care?" *Annals of Internal Medicine* 115(6):486-90, Sept. 15, 1991.

3. Relman, A. "Assessment and Accountability: The Third Revolution in Medical Care." *New England Journal of Medicine* 319(8):1220-2, Nov. 3, 1988.

4. Roper, W., and others. *Effectiveness in Health Care — An Initiative To Evaluate and Improve Medical Practice.* Washington, D.C.: U.S. Department of Health and Human Service, Health Care Financing Administration, pp. 1192-2002, Nov. 1988.

5. Sundwall, D. "Medical Practice Guidelines: Innovation or Failed Initiative?" *American Family Physician* 43(5):184-6, May 1991.

6. *Directory of Practice Parameters.* Chicago, Ill.: American Medical Association, Jan. 1994.

7. Lundberg, G. "Practice Parameter for the Use of Fresh-Frozen Plasma, Cryoprecipitate and Platelets." *JAMA* 271(10): 777-81, March 9, 1994.

8. Agency for Health Care Policy and Research, U.S. Department of Health and Human Services, Public Health Service, *Clinical Practice Guidelines*: Number 14 (Publication No. 95-0462); Number 15 (Publication No. 95-0652); and Number 16 (Publication No. 95-0662).

9. "Interview: Illinois Blue Cross and Blue Shield Medical Director Arnold Widen." *Hospitals and Health Networks* 68(4):50, Feb. 20, 1994.

10. Hannan, E., and others. "Improving the Outcomes of Coronary Artery Bypass Surgery in New York State." *JAMA* 271(10):761-6, March 9, 1994.

11. U.S. Congress. Omnibus Budget Reconciliation Act, 1989. Section 6103. Par. 1, pp. 101-239.

12. *Using Clinical Practice Guidelines to Evaluate Quality of Care.* Vol. I - Issues (AHCPR Pub. No. 95-0045), Vol. II - Methods (AHCPR Pub. No. 95-0048), U.S. Department of Health and Human Services, March 1995.

CHAPTER 18

Practice Variation and Decision Quality:
The Central Role of Patients' Preferences*

by Albert G. Mulley Jr., MD, MPP

emonstration of widespread variation in the use of hospitalization and procedures among geographic areas has had a profound impact on perceptions of the American health care economy and health policy.[1-5] The practice variation phenomenon has been seen differently from different perspectives. A few have focused on possible underutilization among some populations due to poor access or provider bias.[6-8] Others see variation as evidence of poor quality of care, including over- and underutilization.[9] Most observers have focused on variation as evidence of a profound mismatch between the epidemiology of disease and the epidemiology of health care that can be explained by supplier-induced demand for services.[10] Concern about the implications of practice variation for quality and cost has motivated calls for more research to better define effectiveness of common therapeutic interventions and for guidelines to direct and monitor their use.[11-12]

While practice variation has important implications for questions of access, quality, and cost of health care, it raises even more fundamental questions about the process of clinical decision making for individual patients and about the health policy response to the perceived cost-quality dilemma in America.[13-14] How secure is the scientific basis for clinical decisions? What is the purpose of health care? Who establishes personal health care goals? Who defines medical needs and distinguishes them from wants?

Variation in clinical practices among different geographical areas is often attributed to different professional beliefs about the effectiveness of interventions, to financial or other incentives for professionals to provide or withhold care, and to differences in supply of services among geographic areas.[10,15] But practice variation measured from one patient to another may reflect differences in valuations made by or for different people for the same health outcome. Different patients also have different attitudes toward risks, or differences in willingness to accept immediate costs (most important, morbidity and risks of mortality) for future benefits.[16-18] When the purpose of medical care is to

* Work related to this chapter was supported by the Pew Charitable Trust.

improve the quality of life, such variable preferences and attitudes may be the critical determinants of whether an intervention is indicated or not.[19] Variation in medical decision making that reflects individuals' particular preferences is desirable in a society that respects individual differences and autonomy.[20] In the American health care economy, where much of the demand for services is driven by excess supply and where most providers have faced incentives to do more rather than less, matching interventions to patients' well-informed preferences has the potential to reduce utilization rates for common, costly procedures.

The patient's role in decision making and the importance of different patients' different preferences can best be appreciated by considering how lives are affected by common conditions and the treatment decisions that they face. Consider the predicament of a 52-year-old executive with stable angina, a 41-year-old physician with back pain and sciatica due to a herniated lumbar disc, or a 72-year-old carpenter with increasing urinary symptoms due to benign prostatic hypertrophy (BPH). Or consider the decisions faced by a 46-year-old woman with a new diagnosis of early breast cancer, and a 36-year-old man with mild hypertension.

It is evident that these decisions must be made in the face of considerable uncertainty. For the patient with angina, lumbar disc disease, or BPH, the quality of life has been diminished by pain; restricted activity; and, perhaps, the side effects of medical therapy. Surgery is likely to relieve symptoms and thereby improve quality, but the result could also be no important improvement or even a worsening of symptoms. Furthermore, surgery involves a risk of complications; while operative mortality rates for these conditions are generally quite low, such complications could result in death. Obviously, the patient's decision should be very much influenced by the probabilities of these alternative outcomes following surgery and the outcomes that are likely if he or she chooses not to have surgery.

Just as obviously, the decision also depends on how the patient feels about the possible outcomes. The physician can help the patient make the necessary assessments, but it is here that the role of the physician as professional agent is most challenging. Consider that the patient must not only assess the disutility of his or her existing state but must also compare it to possible future states that can only be imagined.

The woman with breast cancer faces these and different issues. Though she is confronted with a deadly disease, a number of alternative therapeutic approaches will, most likely, effect a permanent cure. However, she faces irreducible uncertainty about future recurrence and about possible long-term side effects of some therapies. Her choice depends not only on the best available probabilities of these long-term outcomes, but also on her feelings about the very certain consequences of alternative therapeutic approaches in the near term. While the predicament of the man with risk factors for cardiovascular disease is less compelling, he, too, must make a decision involving trade-offs between near-term morbidity, inconvenience and cost, and reduced probability of serious illness in the distant future.

A decision support system has been developed to assist both doctors and patients as they face such decisions. The computer-based interactive video program is called a Shared Decision-Making Program (SDP).[21] Patients are referred to SDP by their doctors, who supply clinical information at the time of referral to ensure that patients are eligible for SDP. The patient is provided with background reading material and completes a disease-specific health status assessment. Information from the referring doctor and the patient determines the content of SDP for that particular patient. The patient can interact, using a touch-screen monitor, to further tailor the presentation to his or her needs. At the conclusion of the interactive video session, the patient is provided with summary information; a copy is also sent to the referring physician. Post-SDP treatment preferences are recorded, but the patient is advised to defer a final decision until after a return visit to the referring physician. In settings that are participating in SDP-generated outcomes research, the patient is followed regardless of treatment choice.

The conceptual model that underlies SDP responds to the information needs of doctors and patients by creating a closed loop between past patients' outcomes following alternative interventions and current patients who face the same or similar decisions. Past experience may be accessed through published papers or analysis of administrative databases. Alternatively, SDP itself can be used to assemble prospective cohorts, as patients choose between alternative treatments based on their own preferences and attitudes.

Meeting the Needs of Patients
It is often difficult for even the most well-informed clinician to tailor information to the circumstances of a particular patient. Time with the doctor or nurse may be too constrained for full discussion of complex issues. It is evident, then, how SDP can meet the particular information needs of patients. Perhaps more important, SDP can provide a basis for the patient to make informed value judgments. The vicarious experience of other patients, described in their own words, can help patients anticipate what a particular health state will mean for them. SDP programs can also address some of the emotional needs of patients. For example, breast cancer patients can learn not only about the effectiveness and effects of alternative treatments, but also about coping strategies, from women who have used them successfully. The flexibility of the interactive SDP format allows patients to choose to learn more or less about their condition. The emphasis on the shared nature of the decision-making process, with deferral of a final treatment decision to the time of a follow-up visit with the referring physician, allows them to choose their preferred level of decision making responsibility.

Meeting the Needs of the Professional
The most evident responsibility of the clinician in each of the clinical examples is to be aware of the evidence that bears on the effectiveness of alternative treatment options. That is, he or she should be able to provide estimates of the probabilities of good and bad outcomes following different treatment choices. The most obvious source of such probabilities is the experience of previous patients. Because the experience of any one clinician with particular kinds of patients is relatively limited, and because such patients are rarely described in detail or followed carefully after interventions, clinicians rely heavily on published clinical research for such probabilities.

But clinical research has its own limitations. The randomized-control trial, the standard against which other clinical studies are measured, is rarely the source of information for clinical decision making. In the case of BPH, practice evolved without the benefit of published randomized trials comparing surgical and nonsurgical therapy.[22] In the case of lumbar disc disease, there is only one research report.[23] Its 126 patients were randomized to surgery and nonsurgical therapy 20 years ago in Norway. The limits of the professional knowledge base for these two decisions are extraordinary, considering that approximately 300,000 TURPs and 200,000 lumbar surgeries are performed each year in the United States. SDPs, used to assemble prospective cohort studies in representative clinical sites with patients well characterized by those same variables that determine the content of the SDP presentation, provide an opportunity to continuously expand and update the professional knowledge base. Such studies, capturing clinical experience with established and new technologies, could complement randomized trials and other forms of clinical research. In the case of the original SDP, developed for men with BPH, the use of the program, together with common measures of baseline characteristics and outcomes, has produced a cohort study of more than 800 men that has dramatically improved our knowledge of the natural history of BPH.[24]

Clinicians' needs are met when available information, including inevitable uncertainty, can be presented to patients in a consistently balanced and objective manner. Patients who have been provided this information are able to give truly informed consent, based on realistic expectations of potential risks and benefits, and should not be surprised with a suboptimal outcome. Such patients are less likely to seek relief through the tort system, and professional liability exposure for the clinician may be reduced.

Another responsibility of individual clinicians and the profession is to set and maintain standards of performance. Perceived failure to do so has resulted in a large and increasingly intrusive system designed to monitor processes of care and adherence to minimal standards.[9,25] Although there is ample evidence that different providers use different processes of care for the same conditions, and may do so with different degrees of skill, there has been little investment in systems that would describe such differences and relate them to any differences in outcomes.[26-27] Comparative rates of outcomes for the same condition with the same intervention applied by different providers would be an extremely valuable source of information for providers committed to providing high-quality care. SDPs could be used by such providers or networks of providers to assemble and follow cohorts of their own patients and thereby identify rates for good and bad outcomes. Unlike most current quality assurance efforts, outcome studies that included careful attention to measurement of disease severity and comorbidity at baseline could contribute valuable information about effectiveness of alternative interventions (e.g., outcomes following surgical vs. nonsurgical therapy).

Finally, the true professional finds foremost satisfaction in using skills and knowledge to meet the needs of clients—in the case of physicians, patients. SDPs, by providing a balanced presentation of information and vicarious experience as a basis for highly subjective value judgments, provide a measure of assurance that the true needs and wants of the patient will be recognized.

Meeting the Needs of Policy Makers
SDPs can meet the needs of policy makers by improving information about effectiveness of alternative treatments that is generated from follow-up of participants. Even more important, SDPs can inform policy decisions by providing heretofore unavailable

information about how patients value alternative health states and about risks that they are willing and unwilling to take. The approach uncovers the true demand for alternative medical interventions and, thereby, could inform decisions about expanding or reducing the capacity of the health care system to provide those interventions.

Policy makers also have an interest in ensuring and improving the quality of medical care. Providing a system that allows feedback of comparative outcome rate information to providers, to stimulate examination and improvement of processes of care, is another way in which the SDP approach can meet policy needs.

The Need for Research and Development in Decision Quality

A strong presumption for patient autonomy underlies the SDP concept. That presumption rests on the argument that involvement of the patient in decision making will produce intangible benefits derived from a sense of empowerment. A counterargument might be presented by the regret theorist, who would point out that the burden of decision-making responsibility could produce intangible negative effects, particularly if the decision was followed by a bad outcome.[28] Furthermore, there is ample evidence that patients' preferences are exceedingly unstable and can be influenced easily by professional advice or other factors.

Previous studies have shown consistently that most patients want information about their conditions and treatment options and that physicians generally underestimate the degree to which patients wish to be informed.[29] However, a number of other studies suggest that many patients want to delegate decision-making authority to their doctors and that doctors often overestimate the degree to which patients want to bear the responsibility for treatment decisions.[30] These latter studies, however, should be interpreted with caution; little attention was paid to the relationship between information available to patients and their desire for decision-making autonomy. Few people would want the responsibility if they felt their physicians had a superior base of information for decision making. Also, study subjects may not have been given a clear sense that the therapeutic decision should be based on personal preferences as well as matters of fact more readily accessible to the clinician.

Several studies have measured the intangible benefits that may be derived from empowerment and participation in decision making.[31-33] Randomized trials were conducted among patients with peptic ulcer disease and diabetes where the intervention patients were "coached" to be more active during their upcoming office visits. In both cases, the patients were more active and subsequently had statistically higher health and well-being scores than controls in the domains of general health perception, physical functioning, and social/role functioning. These improvements were not associated with changes in symptoms or disease prognosis.

There is also a strong endorsement of professionalism implicit in shared decision making. It has been designed to extend and support the role of doctors in service to their patients. In the spirit of continuous quality improvement, it presumes that physicians are motivated to meet professional obligations and will do so if given sufficient system support and guidance in the form of objective feedback.[34]

The enthusiasm engendered among patients and their doctors by the prototype SDP developed for men with BPH, and the demonstrated decision-making salience of patients' subjective responses to symptoms has led to the development of additional programs. SDPs designed to help patients decide among alternative treatments for low back pain and mild hypertension are currently being used, as are two SDPs developed to help women choose among primary treatments for early-stage breast cancer and decide whether or not to receive adjuvant therapy. The prototype BPH SDP is being revised to reflect new information, including that derived from use of the SDP, about treatment of BPH. A not-for-profit organization, the Foundation for Informed Medical Decision Making, has been incorporated to produce these and future programs and to establish relationships with scientific assessment teams and provider organizations to maintain the accuracy and integrity of the programs and to advance their potential to catalyze outcomes research.

The SDP concept rests on the premise that patients, providers, and society have a common interest in the orderly accumulation and dissemination of information about medical treatment effectiveness and about what patients value in health care. Such information can provide a basis for an informed policy response to the perceived cost-quality dilemma in American health care.

References

1. Wennberg, J., and Gittelsohn, A. "Small Area Variations in Health Care Delivery." *Science* 182(117):1102-8, Dec. 14, 1973.

2. Wennberg, J., and Gittelsohn, A. "Variations in Medical Care among Small Areas." *Scientific American* 246(4):120-34, April 1982.

3. Chassin, M., and others. "Variations in the Use of Medical and Surgical Services by the Medicare Population." *New England Journal of Medicine* 314(5):285-90, Jan. 30, 1986.

4. Chassin, M., and others. "Does Inappropriate Use Explain Geographic Variations in the Use of Health Care Services?" *JAMA* 258(18):2533-7, Nov. 13, 1987.

5. Bunker, J. "Variations in Hospital Admissions and the Appropriateness of Care: American Preoccupations?" *British Medical Journal* 301(6751):531-2, Sept. 15, 1990.

6. Wenneker, M., and Epstein, A. "Racial Inequalities in the Use of Procedures for Patients with Ischemic Heart Disease in Massachusetts." *New England Journal of Medicine* 261(2):253-7, Jan. 13, 1989.

7. Greenfield, S., and others. "Patterns of Care Related to Age of Breast Cancer Patients." *JAMA* 257(20):2766-70, May 22-29, 1987.

8. Held, P., and others. "Access to Transplantation: Has the United States Eliminated Income and Racial Differences?" *Archives of Internal Medicine* 148(12):2594-600, Dec. 1988.

9. Institute of Medicine. *Medicare: A Strategy for Quality Assurance*, Vol. 1. Washington, D.C.: National Academy Press, 1990.

10. Wennberg, J., and others. "Professional Uncertainty and the Problem of Supplier-Induced Demand." *Social Science and Medicine* 16(7):811-24, 1982.

11. Roper, W., and others. "Effectiveness in Health Care. An Initiative to Evaluate and Improve Medical Practice." *New England Journal of Medicine* 319(18):1197-202, Nov. 3, 1988.

12. Wennberg, J. "Dealing with Medical Practice Variations: A Proposal for Action." *Health Affairs* 3(2):6-32, Summer 1984.

13. Mulley, A. "Medical Decision Making and Practice Variation." In Anderson, T., and Mooney, G., Eds. *The Challenges of Medical Practice Variations*. London: MacMillan, 1990.

14. Wennberg, J., and others. "An Assessment of Prostatectomy for Benign Urinary Tract Obstruction. Geographic Variations and the Evaluation of Medical Care Outcomes." *JAMA* 259(20):3027-30, May 27, 1988.

15. Wennberg, J., and others. "Are Hospital Services Rationed in New Haven or Overutilized in Boston?" *Lancet* 1(8543):1185-9, May 23, 1987.

16. Mulley, A. "Assessing Patients' Utilities: Can the Ends Justify the Means?" *Medical Care* 27(3 Suppl):S269-81, March 1989.

17. McNeil, B., and others. "Speech and Survival: Tradeoffs between Quantity and Quality of Life in Laryngeal Cancer." *New England Journal of Medicine* 305(17):982-7, Oct. 22, 1981.

18. McNeil, B., and others. "Fallacy of the Five-Year Survival in Lung Cancer." *New England Journal of Medicine* 299(25):1397-401, Dec. 21, 1978.

19. Mulley, A., and Eagle, K. "What Is Inappropriate Care?" *JAMA* 260(4):540-1, July 22-29, 1988.

20. President's Commission. *Summing Up. The Ethical and Legal Problems in Medicine and Biomedical and Behavioral Research.* Washington, D.C.: President's Commission for the Study of Ethical Problems in Medicine and Biomedical and Behavioral Research, 1983.

21. Kasper, J., and others. "Developing Shared Decision-Making Programs to Improve the Quality of Health Care." *Quality Review Bulletin* 18(6):183-90, June 1992.

22. Barry, M. "Medical Outcomes Research and Benign Prostatic Hyperplasia." *Prostate* 3(Suppl):61-74, 1990.

23. Weber, H. "Lumbar Disc Herniation: A Controlled, Prospective Study with Ten Years of Observation." *Spine* 8(2):131-40, March 1983.

24. Barry, M., and others. "Treatment Choices of Men with Benign Prostatic Hyperplesia Exposed to a Shared Decision Making Program." *Medical Decision Making* 14(4):424, Oct.-Dec. 1994.

25. Vladeck, B. "Quality Assurance through External Controls." *Inquiry* 25(1):100-7, Spring 1988.

26. Wennberg, J, and others. "Use of Claims Data Systems to Evaluate Health Care Outcomes: Mortality and Reoperation Following Prostatectomy." *JAMA* 257(7):933-6, Feb. 20, 1987.

27. Showstack, J., and others. "Association of Volume with Outcome of Coronary Artery Bypass Graft Surgery. Scheduled vs. Nonscheduled Operations." *JAMA* 257(6):785-9, Feb. 13, 1987.

28. Hershey, J., and Baro, J. "Clinical Reasoning and Cognitive Processes." *Medical Decision Making* 7(4):203-8, Oct.-Dec. 1987.

29. Brody, D. "The Patients' Role in Clinical Decision-Making." *Annals of Internal Medicine* 93(5):718-22, Nov. 1980.

30. Strull, W., and others. "Do Patients Want to Participate in Medical Decision-Making?" *JAMA* 252(21):2990-4, Dec. 7, 1984.

31. Greenfield, S., and others. "Expanding Patient Involvement in Care: Effects on Patient Outcomes." *Annals of Internal Medicine* 102(4):520-8, April 1985.

32. Greenfield, S., and others. "Patients' Participation in Medical Care: Effects on Blood Sugar Control and Quality of Life in Diabetes." *Journal of General Internal Medicine* 3(5):448-57, Sept.-Oct. 1988.

33. Kaplan, S., and others. "Assessing the Effects of Physician-Patient Interactions on the Outcomes of Chronic Disease." *Medical Care* 27(3 Suppl):S110-27, March 1989.

34. Berwick, D. "Continuous Improvement as an Ideal in Health Care." *New England Journal of Medicine* 320(1):53-6, Jan. 5, 1989.

CHAPTER 19

Outcomes Measurement: The End or the Beginning?

by Stephen C. Schoenbaum, MD, MPH

The primary mission of health care professionals is to improve health outcomes. If one asks applicants to medical school why they want to become physicians, the usual answer is "to help people." To improve peoples' medical conditions or health status is to improve their outcomes, and to assess peoples' outcomes should be critical to the assessment of their health care.

Building on these simple facts, it seems so logical to think that one can determine whether the care that has been delivered by health system "A" (or Dr. "A") is better than that delivered by health system "B" (or Dr. "B") by simply comparing the health status of patients of "A" and "B." As previous chapters have pointed out (especially see Chapter 10), the situation is not so simple. For one thing, it is necessary to be sure that, at the outset, "A" and "B" were seeing and caring for patients of similar severity or case-mix. If not, the so-called outcomes measurement may not reflect a difference in interventions (or "process") but rather a difference in populations (or "inputs").

In addition, and extremely important, there must be evidence that the interventions play a significant role in changing the outcomes measure that is being applied. Ideally, for gradations of intervention there should be evidence of gradations of outcome—the equivalent of a pharmacologic dose-response curve (which is just one example of a relationship between process or intervention and outcome). An extreme example will demonstrate the problems that occur if there is little relationship between process and outcome: Most dermatologic diseases are not associated with mortality; nor are most dermatologic interventions associated with mortality. For these reasons, one would not expect to see a difference in the mortality rates between a "good" dermatologist and a "poor" one. In fact, it would be inappropriate to compare the quality of care of dermatologists primarily by comparing their mortality rates.

This example makes it apparent that not all types of outcomes measurement are applicable to assessment of all types of care. While it is obviously fallacious to apply mortality rates to the assessment of dermatologic care, it is not so obviously fallacious to apply functional status measurements of asthmatics using a standard measure of functional status (such as the SF-36) to the assessment of asthma care by primary care physicians. Yet, in the instance of the care of asthmatics, there is less known about the physician's ability to change the result of the measurement of functional status than there is known about the relationship between dermatologic practice and mortality. All that is known so far is that asthmatics do not have as good functional status as nonasthmatics when they answer the questions on an SF-36. What is missing is knowledge that, when asthmatics receive more of the "right" interventions from their physicians—the interventions that improve pulmonary function—they have better functional status than asthmatics who receive fewer of the "right" interventions. If that were known, we could compare the functional status of two groups of asthmatics at two points in time and conclude that the group with greater improvement had better care.

Another way to state the problem is to point out that an outcomes measure must be "sensitive" to the process of care. A different example may help the reader with this concept. Consider two groups of arthritic patients who are unable to function fully independently. Both groups have difficulty dressing themselves; both groups have difficulty climbing stairs; and both groups have the same answer to a questionnaire that asks if they are able to function fully independently—"No." One group undergoes a month of occupational therapy (OT) and the other does not. During that month, the OT group learns to use a button-hooker and some other dressing assistance devices. At the end of the month, the persons in the OT group still cannot fully dress themselves, but they can help with the process. They have clearly improved. Yet, when re-asked the question about their functional status, both groups still answer that they cannot function fully independently. That does not mean the intervention, or OT process, is worthless. On the contrary, the functional status question being used in the particular measurement instrument is insensitive to an effective intervention, OT.

In 1988, Paul Ellwood, MD, gave an important and characteristically influential lecture on "outcomes management" to the Massachusetts Medical Society.[1] Although the lecture focused attention on the pivotal issue of measuring and improving or managing patient outcomes, it defined the term "outcomes" as virtually synonymous with measurements of quality of life. Probably owing to Ellwood's lecture, the concept of outcomes measurement has been limited in the minds of many people to measurement of functional status or health status rather than outcomes. Yet, if one is going to measure outcomes and assess health care, one should consider a broad array of outcomes, including not just functional status and health status, but also morbidity and mortality—the traditional outcomes measures in epidemiologic studies.

There are complex interrelationships between different types of outcomes, such as quality of life and survival, and even between different types of the same outcome, such as different aspects of survival. Two classic studies give graphic examples of these interrelationships and trade-offs. One of these studies presented to 37 healthy volunteers information about treatment choices were they to have been discovered to have cancer of the larynx.[2] Surgery, as compared to radiation therapy, sacrifices voice (a consideration in quality of life) for improved three-year survival. Twenty percent of the volunteers expressed a preference for radiation, i.e., favored quality of life over raw survival, demonstrating that some patients do prefer functional status as an outcome over mortality but also illustrating that there is a heterogeneity of patient preferences for outcomes that appropriately would lead to a difference in the clinical intervention applied by clinicians (see Chapter 18).

The other study showed that 12 of 14 patients with lung cancer preferred the option of radiotherapy to surgical excision of the lesion, even though surgery was associated with increased five-year survival.[3] Unlike the study of choices for cancer of the larynx, this preference among patients with lung cancer was not due to quality-of-life considerations during the period of survival but rather to the fact that many of the patients were risk-averse and simply wished to avoid the possibility of an early death due to operative complications. In other words, the trade-off in this study was between two different types of mortality.

The two studies, taken together, provide illuminating evidence that outcomes are complex. Physicians and physician managers will be in a better position to manage clinical care if they understand that relationships between clinical interventions and multiple types of outcome are complex. In fact, by understanding process-outcome relationships and dealing with them in their complexity, one can achieve better outcomes.

Subsequent to his aforementioned lecture, Ellwood's managed care think-tank organization, Interstudy, a piece of which was then spun off into the Health Outcomes Institute, began to make easily available to any health care provider or organization a set of questionnaire instruments called TyPEs (Technology of Patient Experience), each directed to a specific condition, such as diabetes, low back pain, or depression. Perhaps because of this easy access to "outcomes management" instruments, it has become commonplace to think that one can simply amass a useful database of outcomes information by administering such questionnaires at routine patient visits.

Outcomes studies, which epidemiologists call cohort studies, are quite difficult to execute and analyze. Cohort studies generally require a time-series analysis (a typical cohort study example would be a study of survival of patients with a specific malignancy who had received a certain type of chemotherapeutic regimen). One major methodologic problem of such studies is obtaining as complete and accurate follow-up information as possible; another methodologic problem is handling patients who are lost to follow-up in the analysis of the data. It is very difficult to address crucial issues such as these from data obtained at routine patient visits; it is not known whether information obtained from patients who show up for a visit for care is similar to that which might be obtained by a mail questionnaire or standardized telephone interview. Furthermore, whereas clinicians know about patients who have had a visit, they usually do not know which patients have failed to come for follow-up. So, it remains to be determined whether databases obtained from routine care can be mined for important information linking medical care interventions, or process, with outcomes. Early efforts have not been highly productive and remain largely unpublished.

While no measurement is easy, it is usually easier to measure the process of care than the outcomes. Furthermore, one is more likely to find deficiencies in process than in outcome; i.e., not every mistake leads to the patient's dying or having "bad" complications, even though the mistake might have led to a poor outcome. These factors should be taken into account before the primacy of outcomes measurement or the inadequacy of process measurement is accepted or espoused.

Randomized controlled trials (RCTs) are outcomes studies. They are prospective cohort studies in which the intervention, rather than simply being observed and recorded, is actually controlled and administered by the investigators. One way to improve care is to take the results of RCTs in which an intervention that has been shown to improve outcomes (e.g., the use of thrombolytic agents such as tPA within 30 minutes for patients who may have had a myocardial infarction and who have no contraindications to use of the drug); assess the use of the intervention; and, assuming that less than 100 percent of patients who would be expected to benefit from the intervention have been receiving it, increase its appropriate use. Although the measurement of care would be "process" measurement, it would be based on underlying "outcomes" information. In the instance of tPA, many institutions have found that it is possible to decrease the time from a patient's entering an emergency department to administration of the drug.

There is nothing wrong with the approach just outlined, but, to give credit to those who would like to see more observational outcomes studies, a couple of points are worth noting:

- RCTs have significant limitations. In particular, most RCTs have strict entrance requirements for subjects, and there is always the issue of whether the results of the RCT are generalizable to patients who fall outside the original entrance requirements. For example, in the past, many RCTs on important topics such as coronary artery disease included only male subjects, leaving unanswered the question of whether the results were applicable to females.

- Even if the use of an intervention is based on an RCT, it is worth considering an observational study of the actual application of the intervention to be sure that the efficacy seen in the original RCT carries over to clinical effectiveness in actual use. There are many reasons for discrepancies between efficacy demonstrated in carefully controlled and administered trials and use-effectiveness. Fortunately, in the instance of thrombolytic agents such as tPA, some hospitals are beginning to report improved survival of patients in association with more timely administration of drugs.

In the future, there will need to be more measurement of all types if health care delivery is to improve. As clinicians pore over available evidence from observational studies and clinical trials (RCTs) in an effort to develop evidence-based guidelines, they will identify important topics for which there is insufficient existing outcomes information. That circumstance should lead to new RCTs or observational studies.

It would be simpler to gain new information on important clinical topics if clinicians presented an unbiased approach to an intervention—in other words, informed the patient fully about what is not known when trying to obtain consent for a procedure and then kept track of those patients who did and those who did not choose to have the procedure. This is a knowledge-acquisition process that would be facilitated by the development of formal registries rather than depending on informal clinical office-based databases.

To understand this line of thinking, consider the case of coronary angioplasty. When a group of experts were convened by RAND to rate potential indications for the procedure, many of the indications were rated "uncertain."[4] This meant that the experts, based on their own experience and a review of the available literature, either were collectively uncertain that the benefits of the procedure outweighed the risks or disagreed among themselves about whether the benefits outweighed the risks. In effect, there was insufficient outcomes information to make a definite determination of whether the procedure was truly appropriate or inappropriate for certain indications. When the RAND researchers then studied the application of angioplasty in New York, they found that almost 40 percent of the procedures had been performed for "uncertain" indications.[5] Simply following the outcomes of the 40 percent of persons who had angioplasties for "uncertain" indications will yield little knowledge about the benefits versus the risks of angioplasty. Although it is known who had the procedure, it is not known who might have had the procedure and did not, due either to their physicians' unwillingness to offer the procedure or to patients' refusal to have it when offered. To understand the real outcomes of a procedure, one must have comparative information from those who have had the procedure and from those who might have had the procedure but did not.

To acquire better knowledge of the appropriateness of angioplasty for currently "uncertain" indications, one could set up registries of patients who undergo catheterization, have "uncertain" indications for angioplasty, are presented uniform information about what is known about the benefits and risks of the procedure in such circumstances (see Chapter 18), and then choose to have or not have it done. Formal outcomes information would then be collected at standard time intervals following the original catheterization and entered into the registry. The registry would become the basis for a series of prospective cohort studies, and, ultimately, outcomes information would become available for many currently "uncertain" indications.

An important set of considerations for physician executives who understand both clinical issues and management is how best to facilitate setting up and maintaining such registries. A couple of organizations have made early attempts to do just this with projects that, interestingly, grew from their efforts to implement Ellwood's principles of outcomes management. One is the American Group Practice Association, which has implemented specific outcomes measurement projects across a collaborating set of large group practices (e.g., outcomes following hip replacement surgery). Another is the Managed Health Care Association, a group of large employers who have developed partnerships with large managed care organizations (MCOs) to pilot methods for measuring care over time for populations of patients (e.g., asthmatics) enrolled in the MCOs. These efforts have demonstrated that it takes a significant amount of time, effort, and expenditure on the part of all parties to do formal collaborative measurement. Nevertheless, the method has the potential of advancing knowledge and improving care.

Two final notes are in order. The term "outcomes measurement" frequently is used loosely or nonspecifically. It should apply to measurement of outcomes (e.g., health status, mortality, etc) and particularly to the measurement of the relationship between processes and outcomes, but it should not be used to apply simply to the measurement of processes. For example, the percentage of women with newly diagnosed breast cancer whose malignancy is found to be at Stage 0 or Stage 1, is an outcomes measure. Five-year survival following diagnosis of breast cancer is another outcomes measure. The mammography screening rate is a process measure. It is common for people to apply the term "outcomes measurement" to any measurement of care, such as mammography screening rates. That is not helpful. It is confusing. It is also potentially a barrier to better measurement of actual outcomes and their relation to process (e.g., the relationship between detection of early stage malignancies or five-year survival and mammography screening rates).

Second, many persons refer to the cost of care as an "outcome" or outcomes measure. That is an unfortunate and at least partly erroneous simplification. Most of the costs of care are associated with interventions or processes of care rather than with outcomes. There is one component of the total cost of care that is related to outcome—the cost of complications of care, which can also be considered the "cost of poor quality." In general, benefit-cost or cost-effectiveness analyses are formal methods for comparing measurements of the outcomes of care with measurements of the processes of care. In these types of analysis, the costs of care become an aggregate measurement of process of care.

In summary, it is critical that health care providers have better information on the outcomes of the processes of care they apply, but outcomes measurement is neither a simple nor a trivial task. An era of understanding about the nature and complexity of outcomes measurement is just dawning. With improved measurement of outcomes, there will be improved understanding of what processes are effective. With better monitoring of the application of effective processes of care, there will be information to support improvement of care. The net result will be higher quality, more cost-effective care, what all physicians and physician executives should be seeking.

References

1. Ellwood, P. "Outcomes Management: A Technology of Patient Experience." *New England Journal of Medicine* 318(23):1549-56, June 9, 1988.

2. McNeil, B., and others. "Speech and Survival: Tradeoffs between Quality and Quantity of Life in Laryngeal Cancer." *New England Journal of Medicine* 305(17):982-7, Oct. 22, 1981.

3. McNeil, B., and others. "Fallacy of the Five-Year Survival in Lung Cancer." *New England Journal of Medicine* 299(25):1397-401, Dec. 21, 1978.

4. Hilborne, L., and others. *Percutaneous Transluminal Coronary Angioplasty: A Literature Review and Ratings of Appropriateness and Necessity.* Publication JRA-01. Santa Monica, Calif.: RAND, 1991.

5. Hilborne, L., and others. "The Appropriateness of Use of Percutaneous Transluminal Coronary Angioplasty in New York State." *JAMA* 269(6):766-9, Feb. 10, 1993.